KU-351-215

The definitive guide to the leading employers recruiting graduates during 2013-2014.

HIGH FLIERS PUBLICATIONS LTD
IN ASSOCIATION WITH THE TIMES

Published by High Fliers Publications Limited
King's Gate, 1 Bravingtons Walk, London N1 9AE
Telephone: 020 7428 9100 *Web:* www.Top100GraduateEmployers.com

Editor Martin Birchall
Publisher Gill Thomas
Production Director Robin Burrows
Production Manager Grace Proctor
Portrait Photography Sarah Merson

The Times Top 100 Graduate Employers is based on research results from *The UK Graduate Careers Survey 2013*, produced by High Fliers Research Ltd.

Printed and bound in Italy by L.E.G.O. S.p.A.

A CIP catalogue record for this book
is available from the British Library.
ISBN 978-0-9559257-4-0

Contents

THE TIMES
TOP 100
GRADUATE EMPLOYERS

Foreword

By **Martin Birchall**
Editor, *The Times Top 100 Graduate Employers*

Welcome to the fifteenth edition of *The Times Top 100 Graduate Employers*, your guide to Britain's leading employers recruiting graduates in 2013-2014.

During the last twelve months there has been a marked improvement in the graduate job market, with additional vacancies for university-leavers in ten out of fourteen major employment sectors.

One area which has shown especially strong growth is the engineering & industrial sector, where graduate vacancies have increased for the fourth year running and recruitment levels are now 30 per cent higher than in 2009.

"Employers expect to increase their graduate intake by 4.4 per cent during the 2013-2014 recruitment season."

It's little surprise that graduate engineers are in such keen demand – whether it's urban regeneration, electrifying hundreds of miles of the railway network, developing the next generation of nuclear power stations or building new housing, there's no shortage of major engineering challenges to work on.

And Britain's manufacturers are doing well too. The car industry is set to have its best year since 2007 and every part of the manufacturing sector – from aircraft production, to food and drink – expanded during the summer of 2013.

Whilst the improving graduate job market is undoubtedly very welcome news and a sign of the economic recovery that seems to be gathering pace across the country, it's worth remembering that for Britain's most successful employers, recruiting new graduates has always been about developing a steady supply of future managers and leaders for their organisation, rather than simply filling immediate vacancies.

So even during the worst of the recession in 2008 and 2009, very few top employers were keen to break this essential talent pipeline and the vast majority of organisations opted not to shut down their graduate programmes.

This commitment to recruitment has helped the graduate job market recover more quickly than other parts of the economy – entry-level vacancies increased sharply in 2010 and rose again in 2011. The market stalled once more in 2012 but vacancies increased by 4.6 per cent during 2013, taking graduate recruitment to its highest level since 2008.

The latest research with student job hunters shows that confidence is continuing to improve on university campuses too – 44 per cent of final year students from the 'Class of 2013' expected to join the graduate job market straight after leaving university, the highest proportion recorded since 1998. And a record proportion of finalists began researching their career options in the first or second year of their studies, determined to get ahead in the graduate job market.

If you're one of the 350,000 finalists due to graduate in the summer of 2014, then the outlook is also encouraging. Employers featured within this edition of *The Times Top 100 Graduate Employers* expect to increase their graduate intake by 4.4 per cent during the 2013-2014 recruitment season.

Nationally, an estimated five thousand employers are preparing to recruit graduates in the year ahead and more than six hundred organisations have already confirmed that they will be holding recruitment events on campus. With such a wide choice of different types of employment and graduate jobs, how then can prospective employers be assessed and ranked?

To find out, we interviewed 18,252 final year students who graduated from universities across the UK in the summer of 2013, and asked them "Which employer do you think offers the best opportunities for graduates?". Between them, the 'Class of 2013' named organisations in every imaginable employment sector – from the 'Big Four' accounting & professional services firms and City investment banks, to Government departments, media organisations and consulting firms, to IT companies and high street retailers. The one hundred employers who were mentioned most often during the research form *The Times Top 100 Graduate Employers*.

This book is therefore a celebration of the employers who are judged to offer the brightest prospects for graduates. Whether through the perceived quality of their training programmes, the business success that they enjoy, the scale of their organisations, or by the impression that their recruitment promotions have made – these are the employers that are most attractive to university-leavers in 2013.

The Times Top 100 Graduate Employers won't necessarily identify which organisation is right for you – only you can decide that. But it is an invaluable reference if you want to discover what Britain's leading employers have to offer.

Finishing university and finding your first job can be a daunting process but it is one of the most important steps you'll ever take. Having a thorough understanding of the range of opportunities available must be a good way to start.

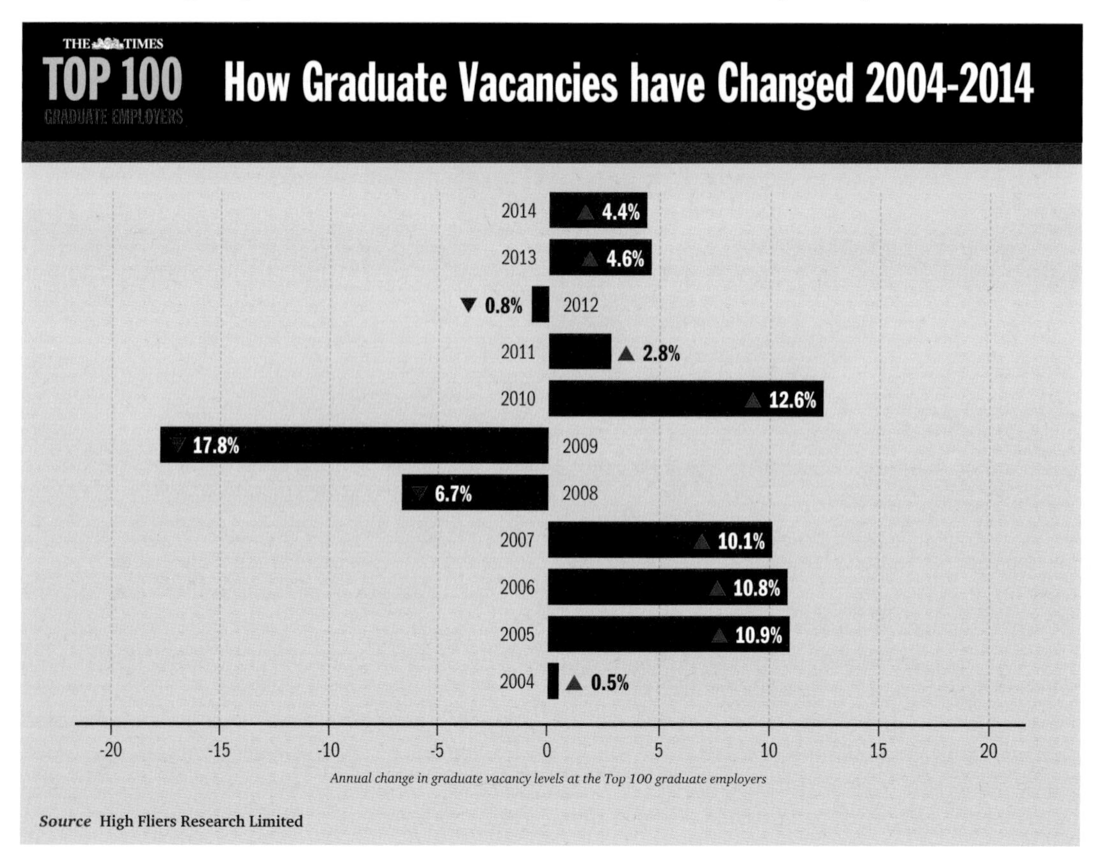

THE TIMES
TOP 100
TeachFirst

Compiling the Top 100 Graduate Employers

By **Gill Thomas**
Publisher, High Fliers Publications

With the British economy finally returning to growth and the graduate job market at its most buoyant since the beginning of the recession, an estimated six-thousand employers are set to hire new graduates from UK universities during the 2013-2014 recruitment season.

Such a wide choice of potential employment to choose from can make identifying the organisation that is 'right' for you quite a daunting challenge. How can you assess the different opportunities and decide which employers offer the best future career paths? What basis can you use to evaluate so many different types of organisations and graduate roles?

"In a remarkable achievement, PwC has now been voted the UK's leading graduate employer for an entire decade."

There are few simple answers to these questions and no single individual employer can ever hope to be right for every graduate – everyone makes their own judgement about the organisations they want to work for and the type of job they find the most attractive.

So how then can anyone produce a meaningful league table of Britain's leading graduate employers? What criteria can define whether one organisation is 'better' than another? To compile the new edition of *The Times Top 100 Graduate Employers*, the independent market research company, High Fliers Research, interviewed 18,252 final year students who left UK universities in the summer of 2013.

These students from the 'Class of 2013' who took part in the study were selected at random to represent the full cross-section of finalists at their universities, not just those who had already secured graduate employment. The research examined students' experiences during their search for a graduate job and asked them about their attitudes to employers.

The key question used to produce the *Top 100* was "Which employer do you think offers the best opportunities for graduates?". This question was deliberately open-ended and students were not prompted in any way. Across the whole survey, finalists mentioned more than 1,100 different organisations – from the smallest local employers, to some of the world's best-known companies. The responses were analysed to identify the number of times each employer was mentioned. The one-hundred organisations that were mentioned most often are the *The Times Top 100 Graduate Employers* for 2013.

It is clear from the considerable selection of answers given by finalists from the 'Class of 2013' that individual students used several different criteria to determine which employer

THE TIMES TOP 100 GRADUATE EMPLOYERS

The Times Top 100 Graduate Employers 2013

	2012			2012	
1.	1	PWC	51.	50	MI5 - THE SECURITY SERVICE
2.	2	DELOITTE	52.	60	MARS
3.	4	TEACH FIRST	53.	48	DEUTSCHE BANK
4.	3	KPMG	54.	65	BOSTON CONSULTING GROUP
5.	7	CIVIL SERVICE	55.	63	BOOTS
6.	5	ALDI	56.	78	BRITISH AIRWAYS
7.	8	EY (FORMERLY ERNST & YOUNG)	57.	77	EXXONMOBIL
8.	6	NHS	58.	56	EUROPEAN COMMISSION (EU CAREERS)
9.	10	JOHN LEWIS PARTNERSHIP	59.	99	DEPARTMENT FOR INTERNATIONAL DEVELOPMENT
10.	14	GOOGLE	60.	46	BT
11.	9	BBC	61.	53	ATKINS
12.	16	BARCLAYS	62.	54	CREDIT SUISSE
13.	19	UNILEVER	63.	79	POLICE
14.	17	BP	64.	59	DLA PIPER
15.	12	TESCO	65.	70	LOCAL GOVERNMENT
16.	11	ACCENTURE	66.	67	BANK OF AMERICA MERRILL LYNCH
17.	13	HSBC	67.	75	PENGUIN
18.	15	GOLDMAN SACHS	68.	100	HOGAN LOVELLS
19.	18	GLAXOSMITHKLINE	69.	74	FOREIGN & COMMONWEALTH OFFICE
20.	24	IBM	70.	NEW	SIEMENS
21.	26	JAGUAR LAND ROVER	71.	57	BAIN & COMPANY
22.	20	J.P. MORGAN	72.	NEW	BAKER & MCKENZIE
23.	21	PROCTER & GAMBLE	73.	NEW	RED BULL
24.	25	ROLLS-ROYCE	74.	58	CO-OPERATIVE GROUP
25.	22	ROYAL BANK OF SCOTLAND GROUP	75.	71	ARCADIA GROUP
26.	23	ARMY	76.	NEW	CHANNEL 4
27.	33	MICROSOFT	77.	62	SANTANDER
28.	30	L'ORÉAL	78.	73	HERBERT SMITH FREEHILLS
29.	35	SHELL	79.	96	EDF ENERGY
30.	40	MCKINSEY & COMPANY	80.	61	UBS
31.	32	LIDL	81.	NEW	COCA-COLA ENTERPRISES
32.	28	MARKS & SPENCER	82.	83	DIAGEO
33.	38	LLOYDS BANKING GROUP	83.	90	GE
34.	31	ALLEN & OVERY	84.	NEW	MORRISONS
35.	41	SKY	85.	86	OXFAM
36.	45	CLIFFORD CHANCE	86.	88	GRANT THORNTON
37.	39	SAINSBURY'S	87.	95	LLOYD'S
38.	34	MORGAN STANLEY	88.	72	ROYAL NAVY
39.	37	ARUP	89.	93	ROYAL AIR FORCE
40.	27	APPLE	90.	87	AIRBUS
41.	36	BAE SYSTEMS	91.	NEW	DANONE
42.	43	LINKLATERS	92.	NEW	BLACKROCK
43.	47	NESTLÉ	93.	NEW	BALFOUR BEATTY
44.	49	SLAUGHTER AND MAY	94.	NEW	NEWTON EUROPE
45.	52	FRESHFIELDS BRUCKHAUS DERINGER	95.	51	NETWORK RAIL
46.	44	CITI	96.	97	MONDELĒZ INTERNATIONAL (FORMERLY KRAFT FOODS)
47.	55	MCDONALD'S	97.	NEW	THOMSON REUTERS
48.	64	ASDA	98.	69	CENTRICA
49.	76	CANCER RESEARCH UK	99.	82	TRANSPORT FOR LONDON
50.	42	WPP	100.	84	NATIONAL GRID

Source High Fliers Research 18,252 final year students leaving UK universities in the summer of 2013 were asked the open-ended question 'Which employer do you think offers the best opportunities for graduates?' during interviews for *The UK Graduate Careers Survey 2013* they considered offered the best opportunities for graduates. Some focused on employers' general reputations – their public image, their business profile or their commercial success.

Others evaluated employers based on the information they had seen during their job search – the quality of recruitment promotions, the impression formed from meeting employers' representatives, or experiences through the recruitment and selection process. Finalists also considered the level of vacancies that organisations were recruiting for as an indicator of possible employment prospects, or were influenced by employers' profile at their university.

Many final year students, however, used the 'employment proposition' as their main guide – the quality of graduate training and development an employer offers, the salary & remuneration package available, and the practical aspects of a first job, such as location or working hours.

Regardless of the criteria that students used to arrive at their answer, the hardest part for many was just selecting a single organisation. To some extent, choosing two or three, or even half a dozen employers would have been much easier. But the whole purpose of the exercise was to replicate the reality that everyone faces – you can only work for one organisation. And at each stage of the graduate job search there are choices to be made as to which direction to take and which employers to pursue.

The resulting *Top 100* is a dynamic league table of the UK's most exciting and well-respected graduate recruiters in 2013.

In a remarkable achievement, the accounting and professional services firm PwC has now been voted the UK's leading graduate employer for an entire decade. The firm polled a total of 7.7 per cent of finalists' votes this year, a lead of more than four-hundred votes over rivals Deloitte, who are in second place for the eighth time.

The widely acclaimed Teach First scheme has moved up one place to reach the top three for the first time, overtaking KPMG, another of the 'Big Four' accounting & professional services firms. The Civil Service has climbed up two places, returning to the top five for the first time since 2010. Aldi and the NHS have both slipped down the ratings but EY (formerly Ernst & Young) has climbed again this year to seventh place, its best ranking so far.

For the seventh consecutive year, the John Lewis Partnership has continued its rise up the rankings, this time to ninth place, just ahead of Google which has seen its vote surge by a almost a third in 2013, taking it into the top ten in the *Top 100* for the first time.

The BBC is now in eleventh place but Barclays has moved up to 12th place, its strongest ever position. Unilever has climbed six places to its highest ranking for seven years and BP has achieved its best *Top 100* rating since 1998. Tesco is down three places and two former top-ten employers, Accenture and HSBC, have fallen further in the latest rankings. Jaguar Land Rover narrowly missed a place in the top twenty but has now risen more than sixty places in just three years.

The highest climbers in this year's *Top 100* are led by the Department for International Development – a new entry in last year's rankings – which has jumped an impressive forty places to 59th place. The city law firm, Hogan Lovells, has climbed thirty-two places to 68th place and Cancer Research UK has moved back up twenty-seven places, following a big drop in the 2012 rankings. But Apple, one of the highest climbers in 2012 has slipped back to 40th place. And there have been major falls too for Network Rail – which is down forty-four places this year to 95th place – and energy firm Centrica which has now dropped more than fifty places in the rankings since 2011.

It has proven to be a difficult year for the leading City banking and financial institutions – just three of the thirteen banks featured within the new *Top 100* have improved their ratings and UBS, Santander and Credit Suisse are among those that have slipped down the rankings.

All three sections of the Armed Forces have again struggled in this year's *Top 100* – the Army has slipped another three places to 26th place, its lowest ever position in the league table. The Royal Navy has dropped a further sixteen places to 88th place and is now ranked just one place ahead of the RAF. Other parts of the public sector have fared a little better – the Police, Local Government and the Foreign & Commonwealth Office have each moved up the rankings.

There are a total of eleven new entries or re-entries in this year's *Top 100*, the highest being Siemens and law firm Baker & McKenzie which return to the rankings in 70th and 72nd places respectively. The energy drinks company Red

Bull, Channel 4, Coca-Cola Enterprises, Morrisons supermarket, asset management firm BlackRock, consumer goods company Danone and consulting firm Newton Europe are each ranked in the *Top 100* for the first time. Infrastructure company Balfour Beatty and media group Thomson Reuters have both reappeared in the *Top 100* in 93rd and 97th places respectively, after dropping out of the list in previous years.

Organisations leaving the *Top 100* in 2013 include Bloomberg, Saatchi & Saatchi, E.ON, Savills, nucleargraduates, Oliver Wyman and four graduate employers that were new or re-entries in last year's rankings – BDO, British Sugar, Norton Rose and Towers Watson.

This year's edition of *The Times Top 100 Graduate Employers* has produced a number of significant changes within the rankings and the results provide a unique insight into how graduates from the 'Class of 2013' rated the UK's leading employers. Almost all of these organisations are featured in the 'Employer Entry' section of this book – from page 55 onwards, you can see a two-page profile for each employer, listed alphabetically for easy reference.

The editorial part of the entry includes a short description of what the organisation does, its opportunities for graduates and its recruitment programme for 2013-2014. A fact file for each employer gives details of the business functions that graduates are recruited for, the number of graduate vacancies on offer, likely starting salaries for 2014, their minimum academic requirements, application deadlines, the universities that the employer is intending to visit during the year, plus details of their graduate recruitment website and how to follow the employer on Facebook, Twitter and LinkedIn. The right-hand page of each employer entry contains a display advert promoting the organisation.

If you would like to find out more about any of the employers featured in *The Times Top 100 Graduate Employers*, then simply register with **www.Top100GraduateEmployers.com** – the official website showcasing the latest news and information about *Top 100* organisations.

Registration is entirely free and as well as being able to access the website, you'll receive regular email updates about the employers you are most interested in – this includes details of the careers events they're holding at your university during the year, up-and-coming job application deadlines, and the very latest business news about the organisations.

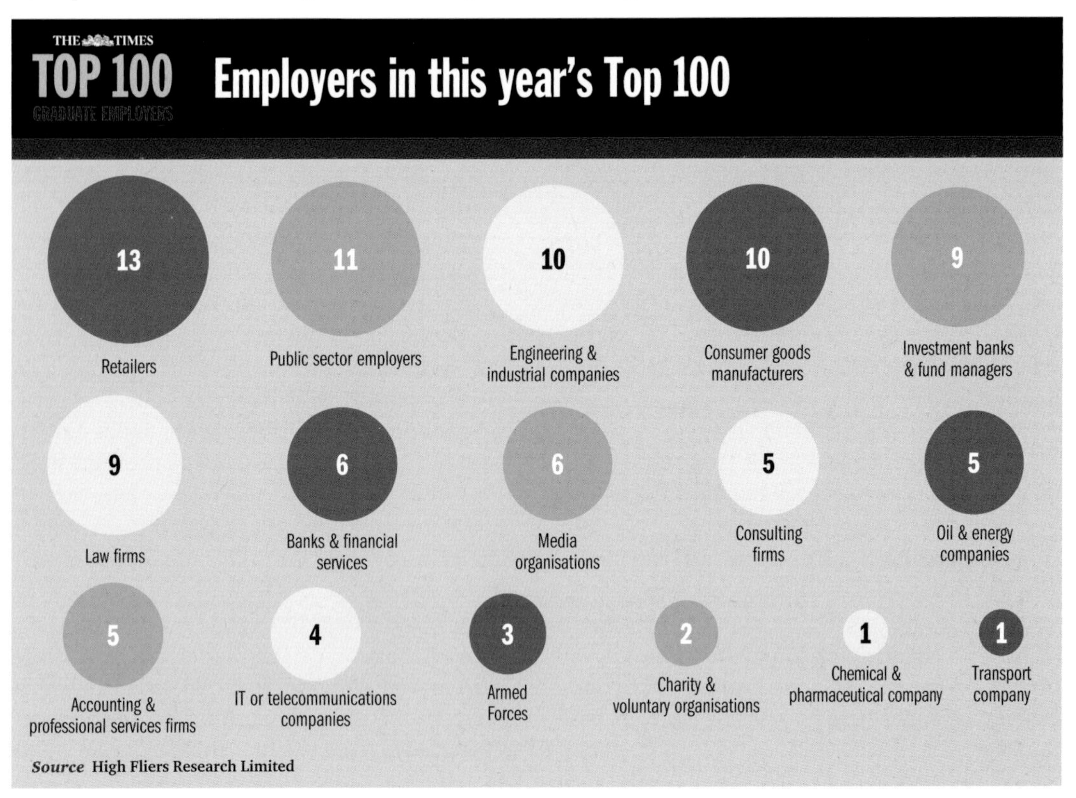

Graduate recruitment reaches highest level since 2008

Richard Adams
Education editor

ing the top graduate pay brackets. Aln
twice as many men

Stu
the
sinc
desp
fierc
A
large
- inc

Graduate outlook bes since 2008

By

Experience gets graduates top jobs

Graduate job at 5-year hig

The public sector has driv
rise in graduate recruitment
a 72 per cent rise in number
taken on in the past five yea
The graduate intake at

Top employers pick graduates who worked during studies

Nicola Woolcock

this rises to more than half of jobs.
The research found that more inter

Banking boom turns to student gloo as job market for graduates stagnate

Students, take note: firms give the best jobs to former interns

MORE than one in three graduates taking jobs at leading firms have already done work experience for their employer.
The record level of 36 per
revealed

By Laura Clark
Education Correspondent

scramble ... ps. This year more

Graduates floc to teacher post

TEACHER training charity Te
First is the largest recruiter of
graduates in the country, bea
the Army and the Civil Service
The charity

Graduate jobs on the rise but it's still a fight

Students who become interns stand out in th graduate jobs market

By Graeme Paton, Education Editor

STUDENTS who take an internship are three times more likely to win a good job as the competition for graduate positions

Pay gap Female graduates expect lower salaries

Female graduates expect "substantially" less pay than their male counterparts, a report shows, prompting concerns that w
could be le

of standing out in the jobs ma
research by the London Sch
nomics found that students
degree – a 2:1 or better – ea
£2,000 a year more than clas
narrowly ga a 2:2.
The

Graduates feel confident over job prospects

By Richard Garner
EDUCATION EDITOR

The class of 2013 are the most optimistic over their prospects of gaining

search for full-time employment before starting their final year at
versity. On average, they made
applications for a job each.
The survey, conducted by Hi

Outlook sour for graduates without work experience

The number of jobs awaiting g
uates slumped in 2012, after tv

Understanding the Graduate Job Market

By **Martin Birchall**
Managing Director, High Fliers Research

As the long, slow recovery from the economic slump that has affected every part of Britain's economy over the last six years finally gathers momentum, new graduates who left university in the summer of 2013 will have seen increasingly cheerful newspaper headlines about the graduate employment market.

The country's leading employers stepped up their entry-level recruitment by a better-than-expected 4.6 per cent in 2013, taking the number of graduate positions on offer to its highest level since 2008.

This very welcome news contrasted sharply with the dip in graduates vacancies during 2012 when, despite the 'feel good' factor from the London Olympics and the Queen's Diamond Jubilee, the job market was hit by fears of a double-dip recession and weakening business confidence.

"In 2014, the Teach First programme is expected to be the biggest individual employer of graduates, with 1,550 places."

The outlook for graduates from the 'Class of 2014' is a positive one too – the latest analysis shows that vacancies at the leading graduate employers are set to rise by a further 4.4 per cent in 2014. More than a third of the organisations in the *Top 100* plan to hire more graduates this year than they did in 2013 and two-fifths believe they will take a similar volume of recruits, while a quarter expect to reduce their graduate intake, albeit usually by a small number of roles. Together, the employers in this year's *Top 100* are advertising a total of 17,901 jobs, compared to the 17,146 graduates these organisations hired in 2013.

Once again, this year's graduate recruitment is set to be dominated by the country's largest accountancy & professional services firms, which are preparing to recruit 4,000 new trainees in 2014, a 5 per cent increase on their graduate recruitment during 2012-2013.

For the fifth consecutive recruitment season, the number of graduate roles at the UK's most sought-after engineering & industrial employers is expected to increase, taking recruitment levels to within just 5 per cent of the number of entry-level jobs available in the sector before the start of the downturn in 2008.

Graduate employers in a total of eleven of the fifteen industries and business sectors represented within *The Times Top 100 Graduate Employers* are optimistic about graduate recruitment in 2014. The UK's best-known retailers are planning to recruit up to a fifth more graduates in the coming year and there are healthy increases in vacancies too at the consulting firms, consumer goods manufacturers, and oil & energy companies.

Within the media, transport and chemical & pharmaceuticals sectors, vacancy numbers are unchanged but there are likely to be slightly fewer

graduate opportunities at the leading law firms, in the Armed Forces, at the City's investment banks & fund managers, and at IT & telecommunications companies in the year ahead.

On average, employers featured within the *Top 100* are offering 180 graduate vacancies each for 2014 but a quarter of organisations plan to hire at least 250 new recruits and three employers anticipate recruiting well over 1,000 university-leavers during 2013-2014.

Although general recruitment remains restricted within many parts of the public sector, the eleven Government departments and agencies appearing in the latest *Top 100* rankings are planning to step-up their graduate intake by another 10 per cent in 2014 – the fourth time in five years that recruitment of graduates has increased within the public sector.

The continuing major expansion of the Teach First programme means that for the second year running, it is expected to be the biggest individual employer of graduates in *The Times Top 100 Graduate Employers* in 2014, with 1,550 places available. Other substantial recruiters include the accounting & professional services firms PwC and Deloitte (1,200 vacancies each), the Civil Service Fast Stream (800 vacancies), EY (700 vacancies) and the Army (650 vacancies).

Almost two-thirds of the employers featured in this year's *Top 100* have vacancies for graduates in IT, at least half have opportunities in financial management or human resources, two-fifths

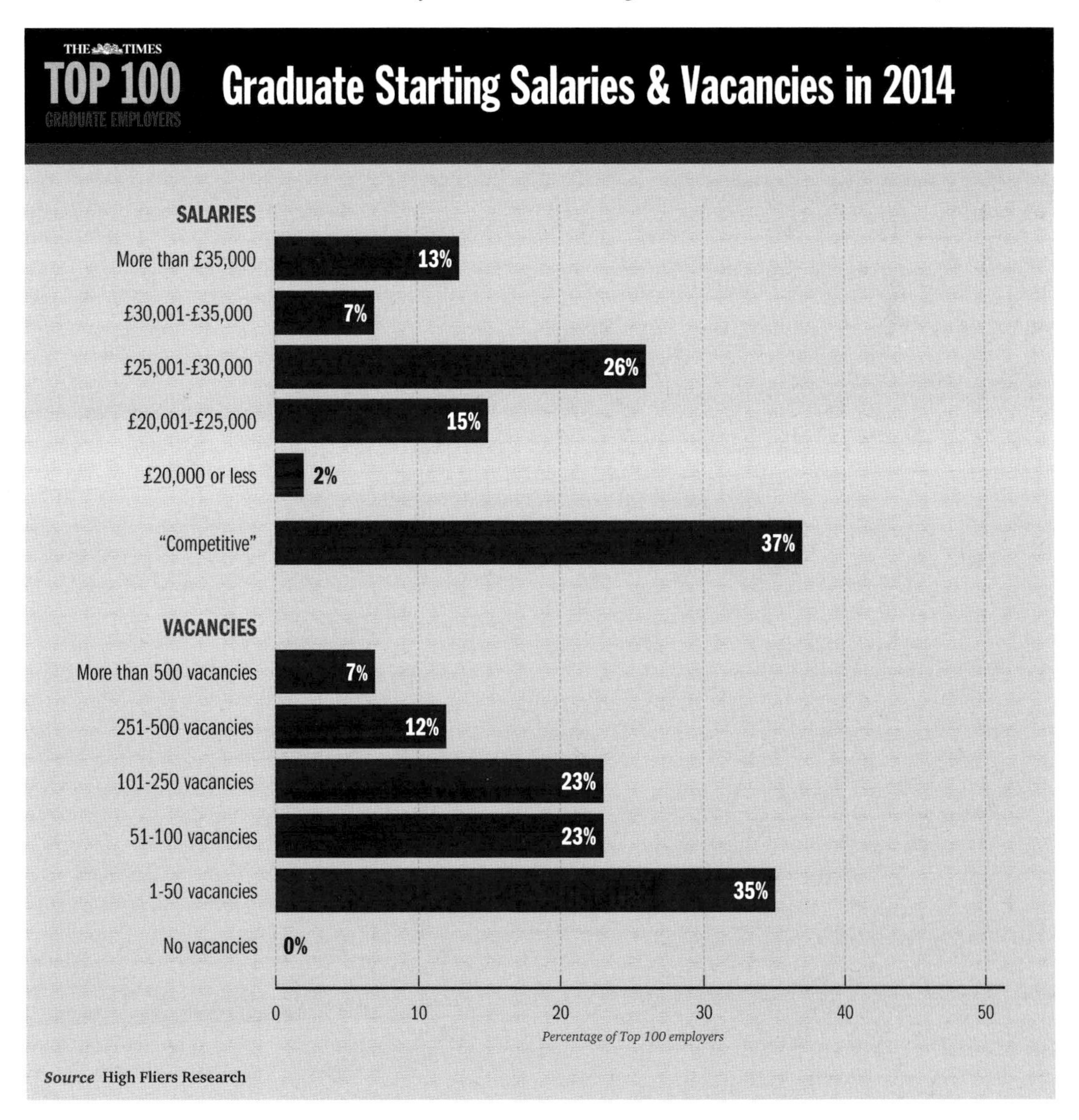

are recruiting for marketing roles, over a third are hiring engineering or general management graduates, a quarter are looking for recruits to work in sales, research & development or purchasing, whilst a fifth want retail personnel or have roles in consulting.

More than ninety of the *Top 100* employers have graduate vacancies in London and over half have posts available elsewhere in the south east of England. More than half also have graduate roles in the north west of England, the Midlands and Scotland. Northern Ireland, Wales and East Anglia have the fewest vacancies.

For the last four years, the average graduate starting salary at Britain's leading employers has remained unchanged at £29,000 and more than three-quarters of the organisations featured in this year's edition of *The Times Top 100 Graduate Employers* have again opted to leave their graduate starting salaries for 2014 unchanged from 2013 rates. Fewer than a sixth of employers have announced increases to their graduate packages for 2013, typically by four per cent or less.

Almost two-fifths of *Top 100* employers simply describe their salary packages for next year as "competitive". Fewer than a fifth expect to offer new graduates up to £25,000 when they begin work and thirteen organisations – mainly City investment banks, law firms or the leading oil & energy companies – are planning to pay starting salaries in excess of £35,000. The most generous graduate packages publicised within this edition of the *Top 100* are again at the European Commission, which offers new graduates a salary of at least £41,500, and retailer Aldi who continues to offer its recruits a sector-leading starting salary of £40,000 and an Audi A4 car.

Around half of the UK's leading employers now recruit graduates year-round (or in different phases during the year) and will accept applications throughout the 2013-2014 recruitment season, until all their vacancies are filled. For employers with a single application deadline, many are in either November or December, although the leading law firms usually have July closing dates.

More than seven out of ten *Top 100* employers insist that applicants for their graduate programmes should have a 2.1 degree or better and a quarter now specify a minimum UCAS tariff too, typically in the range of 260 to 340 – the equivalent of 'BCC' to 'AAB' at A-level.

This means, therefore, for those who make the grade, there continues to be an excellent range of career opportunities and some great starting salaries on offer from *The Times Top 100 Graduate Employers* in 2014.

THE TIMES TOP 100 GRADUATE EMPLOYERS

Graduate Vacancies at Top 100 Employers in 2014

	2013		NUMBER OF VACANCIES	% OF TOTAL VACANCIES	CHANGE SINCE 2013
1.	1	**ACCOUNTANCY & PROFESSIONAL SERVICES FIRMS**	4,000	**22.3**	**▲ 5.1%**
2.	3	**PUBLIC SECTOR EMPLOYERS**	3,280	**18.3**	**▲ 10.9%**
3.	2	**INVESTMENT BANKS & FUND MANAGERS**	1,865	**10.4**	**▼ 1.6%**
4.	4	**ENGINEERING & INDUSTRIAL COMPANIES**	1,615	**9.0**	**▲ 3.4%**
5.	6	**RETAILERS**	1,590	**8.9**	**▲ 20.5%**
6.	5	**BANKING & FINANCIAL SERVICES**	1,240	**6.9**	**▲ 0.7%**
7.	7	**ARMED FORCES**	1,050	**5.9**	**▼ 5.6%**
8.	8	**LAW FIRMS**	714	**4.0**	**▼ 6.1%**
9.	9	**IT & TELECOMMUNICATION COMPANIES**	600	**3.4**	**▼ 1.6%**
10.	10	**CONSULTING FIRMS**	600	**3.4**	**▲ 11.7%**
11.	11	**OIL & ENERGY COMPANIES**	500	**2.8**	**▲ 3.1%**
12.	13	**CONSUMER GOODS MANUFACTURERS**	423	**2.4**	**▲ 6.3%**
13.	12	**MEDIA ORGANISATIONS**	368	**2.1**	NO CHANGE
14.	14	**TRANSPORT COMPANIES**	70	**0.4**	NO CHANGE
15.	15	**CHEMICAL & PHARMACEUTICAL COMPANIES**	50	**0.3**	NO CHANGE

Source High Fliers Research

Careers and Employability
Direct your
future
TOP 100
TOP 100
TOP 100

Successful Job Hunting

By **Helen Smith**
Head of Careers and Employability, Loughborough University

There really is no such thing as starting too early when it comes to planning your career. Years ago looking for a graduate job was something students did in the final year of a degree course but now, in the era of higher tuition fees and a highly competitive graduate job market, it's not unusual for students to begin researching their options as soon as they arrive at university.

A great first step is to make contact with your university careers service. Universities across the UK provide careers information and guidance to their students so go and find your careers centre, have a look at the services they can offer and talk to the information staff. Their key aim is to ensure students get the best possible careers advice, so don't delay, and don't be put off if you're worried that 'I don't know what I want to do after university'; that's the perfect time to explore your options.

"You are unlikely to get access to such great guidance ever again in your career, so make the most of it now."

Careers services provide a wealth of support and on your first visit the information staff should be able to answer your questions and show you some of the available resources. These could include details of the career destinations of recent graduates from the university, information on careers presentations and workshops, copies of printed guides to different industries and career sectors that you can take away, and all sorts of handouts giving tips on topics like how to create a great CV, or writing positive job applications.

Information staff can also help you make the most of the comprehensive information and advice that's likely to be available on your university's careers website, such as details of local careers events, the latest employer vacancies, information about internships and work placements, and background reading about a wide range of individual career paths and employment areas. Make sure too that you register to receive regular email updates from your careers service – at a number of universities this is automatic for all students but elsewhere you might need to activate this yourself.

At any stage, from your first year to your last, you will also benefit from speaking to one of your university's careers advisers. They will be specialists in graduate careers and are usually highly experienced and professionally qualified, so whether you book a 'quick advice' session, typically lasting 10-15 minutes, or a longer 'consultation' appointment, you will get some one-to-one time to discuss your particular questions and potential career options. Careers advisers may be available on a drop-in basis, and sometimes they might be based in your academic department, but during the busiest weeks of the

autumn term you'll probably need to book ahead to get a suitable appointment.

I can't emphasise enough how important it is to use this service – you are unlikely to get access to such great guidance ever again in your career, so make the most of it now. It's one of the undoubted benefits of attending a good university. Careers services are there to help you make the best possible start to your career, and to help you develop career management skills that will help you at every stage of your working life. It's great advice – please don't skip it.

So, your careers adviser will help you explore the graduate job market you'll be entering and guide you through the decision-making process to help you identify the opportunities that will suit you best. Their role is to develop your awareness, your self-confidence and your skills to give you the ability to decide for yourself what you want from your career. They will help you devise a plan of action as you research your options, start to make job applications and progress through the recruitment process. They can also help you manage any setbacks and get back on the path to success – it's what careers advisers are good at, and ultimately nothing makes us happier than seeing students succeed.

Understanding the huge range of opportunities available to graduates can be quite a challenge. The job market now moves very, very fast and some of today's graduate opportunities simply didn't exist ten years ago and certainly weren't there when your parents were graduating from university or considering their future careers. There are numerous industries and sectors that recruit graduates each year and whilst many university-leavers are attracted to the graduate programmes at well-known organisations including those featured in *The Times Top 100 Graduate Employers*, others will find roles with smaller and medium-sized enterprises (SMEs), and some of today's graduates will pursue far less structured career paths than was usual in previous generations.

Depending on your interests and skills, there are different ways to approach your job search. You could focus on particular job functions, such as working as a researcher, an accountant or in marketing or human resources, or you could look into specific industries like sports, the arts, manufacturing or banking. Whichever route you take, there is a mass of information available online about graduate roles, career sectors and potential employers – the challenge is navigating your way through it all and avoiding information overload.

Researching companies via LinkedIn and other social media can also be a brilliant way to begin building a professional network of contacts. Your careers service can help you set yourself up on LinkedIn appropriately and guide you as to how to manage your networks, how to learn from them, and how to make the most of your new contacts. Start early and small-scale and over the months and years you'll develop a massively useful network.

Once you've begun looking into individual employers, look out for the many careers events and activities that will be taking place at your university. Virtually every major university hosts a number of careers fairs during the year which are a great way to meet different employers. Some fairs follow a specific theme, such as engineering or finance, but at the largest events you might see hundreds of employers exhibiting together, most of whom will usually be interested in meeting students and graduates from any subject area.

The best advice for getting the most out of fairs is prepare, prepare, prepare – it's essential to do some research before you get to the event. Check which employers are attending, find out what they do and what kind of graduate roles they're offering, particularly as there may well be some great organisations targeting your university who might not be familiar names. Being able to go up to a stand and say 'I understand you look for graduates who are interested in...' will help you start a conversation with an employer. Some of the company representatives you'll meet may be alumni of your university, so it's a great opportunity to engage with someone who can talk about how they got through the application and selection process and explain the work they're doing now.

The first impression you make at these events can make a real difference, so don't underestimate the potential impact you could have if you ask intelligent questions and demonstrate you've done some research beforehand. It's not unusual for employers to jot down the name of students they're impressed with, so they can look out for them when they make an application and tag them as someone they're particularly interested in.

Many employers also visit universities to hold their own presentations, something which recruiters see as a key part of the process of attracting the right calibre of students to apply for their graduate programmes. The format of these employer presentations or events varies considerably but most will give a valuable insight into their company, the graduate jobs available, their application process, and what they look for in their graduate recruits. Presentations often take place in the early evening and might also include a networking session which can be a great opportunity to chat to the employer's representatives, get a feel for the culture of the organisation and find out 'are these the type of people I could see myself working with?'. Again, make sure you prepare well for these events, be ready to network and think about a few questions you want to ask. And dress as if you were going to a meeting rather than a social event – you need to make the right impression with your potential future employer.

There are other ways to meet with employers. Some hold informal 'drop-in' sessions for students to talk to recruiters and recent graduates, whilst others employers host skills training events where recruiters and managers provide coaching on specific business skills, like leadership, team-working and problem-solving, or give tips on aspects of graduate recruitment process, such as CV writing, making applications, interviews or assessment centres. Whatever the format, use as many opportunities as you can to connect with employers.

Once you've pinpointed which career areas or placement opportunities you're interested in and the employers you'd be keen to work for, the next step is to begin making applications. There's no magic number for how many to make – the reality is you'll make as many applications as you need to in order to secure the role you want. The challenge is to make sure they are good quality applications and that does mean you'll need to set aside quite a bit of time to work on them. It can take several hours to compile all the required information and prepare your answers to employers' questions.

Before you start filling in your first application, it's really helpful to update your CV so that it includes all your academic and extra-curricular achievements, as well as the skills you've developed during university. Remember: being successful isn't only about your degree result, employers are just as keen to hear about all the other things you've done during your studies, your work experience and even some of what you did at school. Don't be afraid to go back to your careers service for help at this stage – most run a programme of workshops, presentations and one-to-one sessions on CV writing and how to market yourself effectively. Once you've built up your CV, it's a really useful reference to draw upon when you're completing employers' online application forms and for many smaller graduate employers, a CV with a covering letter is still the main way to apply.

If you're applying to one of the larger national or international employers, then it's likely they'll have a three-or-four-stage selection process. During your initial application, you may be asked to complete one or more online ability or personality tests. These numeracy, reasoning and psychometric tests can seem quite daunting and unfamiliar, so are well worth practising beforehand. Your careers service can help you become familiar with the kind of tests you could face and as with most things, the more you practise the tests, the better you are likely to become.

Provided your initial application is successful, the next stage in the selection process is likely to be an interview, either over the telephone or face-to-face. At this point, preparation can make an enormous difference to how well you do, and your careers service may offer mock interviews and training sessions on what to expect.

Ultimately there are three things that employers are trying to find out from an interview – 'does this person have the skills we're looking for?', 'is this person suited to our organisation?' and 'what value are they likely to add?'. They will of course ask a great many more questions than this, but at the core that's what they're trying to discover. Remember, if you've made it through to a first interview then you're doing very well – your application has stood out from the others and the employer is already interested in you, so try to provide the evidence they need to answer these three questions positively.

An interview might be the final stage, but for most of the larger graduate recruiters it's likely that if you do well at the interview you'll then be invited to a final-round assessment centre. These take many different forms but will often include some sort of group exercise, more tests, an individual exercise or presentation, further interviews and informal assessments. This can last anything

ROYAL
NAVY
YOU
CONTROL A
WARSHIP NOT
CTRL ALT DELETE
THALES

ROYAL NAVY OFFICER

Being an officer in the Royal Navy is a career like any other, but the circumstances and places are sometimes extraordinary. With opportunities ranging from Engineer Officer to Medical Officer, it's a responsible, challenging career that will take you further than you've been before. If you want more than just a job, join the Royal Navy and live a life without limits.

LIFE WITHOUT LIMITS
08456 07 55 55
ROYALNAVY.MOD.UK/CAREERS

from half a day to a full two-day experience with an overnight stay and a formal dinner. The golden rule for assessment centres is to assume that you're being assessed through every part of them, even in the coffee breaks and through lunch – it's likely that everyone you meet during the process will be asked for their opinion of you, even recent graduates and receptionists.

At this final stage, one area that students often struggle with is explaining why they want to work for that particular company or organisation. It's not sufficient to simply say you just need a job, or that you want a job in banking or engineering; you'll be expected to articulate clearly why you're keen on working for that specific bank or engineering company. It's a really tough question to tackle but it's one you need to be ready for – do your research, and the recruiters will be impressed if you're informed, articulate and passionate about their organisation.

Employers usually make job offers quite quickly after assessment centres so you shouldn't have to wait long to hear if you've been successful. If you're in the very fortunate position of having more than one job offer, you might want to talk through your final decision as to which offer to accept.

Your careers adviser can help you reflect on what you've seen of the different organisations during the selection process, the variations in company cultures, and what the practical differences may be between the job offers. Don't feel pressured to accept an offer before you've weighed up your options, most employers will understand you need some thinking time.

If you don't get a job offer or don't make it into the later rounds of the selection process, then don't panic. Try and work out where you might have gone wrong or where you believe you could have done better – it's just like taking an exam where you didn't quite get the grade you were hoping for.

Identify how you could improve or hone your applications next time or do more preparation for the tests or interviews. Even if you make a further round of applications later on, there will still be many good graduate opportunities out there. Quite a lot of employers don't necessarily fill all their places in their first round of recruitment, and some may well re-open their applications again in the summer. And companies that only recruit a few placement students or graduates might even wait until later in the academic year to start recruiting, so all is not lost.

Remember, there is an element of luck within the graduate recruitment process and it may be that you've made a great application, done well through the selection rounds and got incredibly close to offers, but for whatever reason it just hasn't worked out. Try not to blame yourself – ultimately persistence pays, so if you just pick yourself up, dust yourself down, learn and move on to the next application, you will be successful in the end.

Every good careers adviser will also remind you that some of the most successful careers are built on a false start or two. It might take a while to find your ideal job, but with your degree behind you, you'll have more options than most – and provided you persevere and keep learning from your experiences, eventually it will happen.

THE TIMES TOP 100 GRADUATE EMPLOYERS

Where the Graduates of 2013 wanted to Work

	2012		% OF FINALISTS		2012		% OF FINALISTS
1.	1	MARKETING	15.6%	11.	10	SALES	8.5%
2.	3	MEDIA	14.0%	12.	11	HUMAN RESOURCES	8.0%
3.	5	CONSULTING	13.5%	13.	12	FINANCE	7.6%
4.	2	TEACHING	13.2%	14.	14	GENERAL MANAGEMENT	6.9%
5.	4	CHARITY OR VOLUNTARY WORK	12.0%	15.	15	RETAILING	5.6%
6.	7	RESEARCH & DEVELOPMENT	11.8%	16.	16	BUYING OR PURCHASING	4.5%
7.	6	INVESTMENT BANKING	11.7%	17.	17	IT	3.9%
8.	8	ACCOUNTANCY	10.8%	18.	18	ARMED FORCES	2.7%
9.	9	LAW	9.6%	19.	20	TRANSPORT OR LOGISTICS	2.6%
10.	13	ENGINEERING	8.6%	20.	19	ACTUARIAL WORK	2.3%

Source **High Fliers Research** 18,252 final year students leaving UK universities in the summer of 2013 were asked which sectors they had applied to or planned to apply to for graduate jobs, during interviews for *The UK Graduate Careers Survey 2013*

TACKLING
CAREER F

milkround

pwc

Celebrating Ten Years as Britain's Number 1 Employer

By **Charles Macleod**
Head of Global Sourcing, PwC

When I left university in 1982 with a degree in geography, I did what many of my generation did and stumbled into accountancy.

There was no talk in those days of 'employers of choice' or league tables ranking graduate programmes and joining an accounting firm was seen by many new graduates as something of a delaying tactic because the professional training for accountancy had a very similar structure to university life. It lasted three years, you had a large peer group who joined when you did, you all went to slightly different places, but everyone studied for exams together and met up for training courses – you just didn't have the long vacations or quite as much fun with subsidised alcohol.

"We hired a model airship, covered it in PwC logos and flew it around the top of all the other employers' careers stands."

At that point there were eight large accountancy firms and having applied to several of them, I found myself through to the final selection round with two of the top firms. I opted to join Price Waterhouse because I'd liked everyone I'd met at the firm during the recruitment process – and I simply didn't have the same reaction to the people I'd met at the other firms. So I came to Price Waterhouse and although I loved the firm, I realised that I did not wish to be an accountant and left to pursue a career in the recruitment industry.

I returned to the firm ten years later because I'd rather outgrown the cut and thrust of the recruitment agency world and was looking for fresh challenges. By the mid-1990s, the accountancy profession had changed considerably and a series of mergers had reduced the number of major firms to six – Arthur Andersen, Coopers & Lybrand, Deloitte & Touche, Ernst & Young, KPMG Peat Marwick and Price Waterhouse. Price Waterhouse itself had grown substantially, with more businesses and five or six different entry points and training schemes for new graduates, compared with the single chartered accountancy training route that was on offer when I'd graduated.

But even by the time the first league table of *The Times Top 100 Graduate Employers* was produced in 1997 – the year before Price Waterhouse merged with Coopers & Lybrand to form PricewaterhouseCoopers – just one accountancy firm was ranked within the top ten and university students regularly described the profession and the firms within it as 'dull', 'boring' and 'traditional'.

When I was asked to head up recruitment in the merged firm, I remember sitting in a graduate recruitment presentation at the University of Warwick thinking that this is PowerPoint slide

From flying an airship at careers fairs, to projecting careers messages onto buildings and providing free coffee for students, PwC's strategy has been to make an impact on campus

number fifty-four and I still haven't seen anything distinctive. The students were getting restless and those that were still attentive had their eye on the food and drink and not the slides. I thought there and then – we must be able to do something more exciting than this and that proved to be the spark for the campaign that followed.

Our biggest single challenge was that we have a proposition for graduates that goes across all degree subjects and we just weren't getting that across – people were thinking they'd got to have studied accounting to come and work for us. Because we didn't have a consumer brand, few students had any awareness of the firm before they went to university. So we decided we had to do something that was really unusual, something which would surprise people and fundamentally appeal across all degree subjects.

The 'One for All' campaign that followed – positioning the firm as the number one employer for all university graduates – was about capturing people's imaginations. In that first year, we took coffee and buns to students before lectures in the winter and offered free post-exam massages in the summer. People were absolutely fascinated by it and I overheard a lovely quote from one bemused student who said, "I've no idea who they are but I'm going to go away and find out!".

The beginning of the campaign coincided with the emergence of social media and a wave of new technology. I remember listening to Radio Four one day in early 2002 and they were talking about a podcast and so I came into the office and asked 'what's a podcast, we've got to do a podcast'. Nobody had any idea what I meant, but we were the first firm to do one. We were also one of the earliest employers to deliver recruitment information directly to students and graduates through their mobile phones.

Reaching number one in *The Times Top 100 Graduate Employers* came much quicker than any of us had expected. Sitting in the audience of *The Times Graduate Recruitment Awards* in 2004 where the new rankings were being counted down I hit that awful moment when number two had been announced and our name still hadn't come up – leaving me thinking we were either out of the list altogether or this is really, really good news.

Becoming the 'graduate employer of choice' at the UK's top universities was amazing recognition for the success that our campaign had had but it also helped underline just how essential recruiting the right graduates was for our business. An organisation like ours is little more than the collective wit and wisdom of our people – so hiring the best people with the right attributes is always going to be important to us.

As our recruitment campaign developed, we made a very clear commitment to spending a lot of time on campus. We invested heavily in putting our people on the ground at universities, running up to seven-hundred local events each recruitment season – it's a lot of hours, a lot of miles, but it's all about developing relationships with potential recruits. Having a recognisable brand raises awareness but recruitment success comes through the relationships that you build – it has always been important that students and graduates should take as much time as they want before deciding to apply or accept a job offer with us.

Our marketing, particularly in the early stages of our campaign, was all about being innovative and exciting. For example, we'd noticed that careers fairs often happen in large university venues which usually only occupied the bottom ten feet of the space in the hall. So we hired a model airship, covered it in PricewaterhouseCoopers logos and flew it around the top of all the other employers' careers stands. It caused havoc with the rest of the recruiters but was fabulous fun.

That sense of fun extended to our advertising and recruitment brochures too, with pictures of trapeze artists, people standing on their heads and people jumping into piles of leaves – the exact opposite of what might be expected of an accountancy firm. We projected the firm's logo onto the sides of university buildings up and down the country and jet-washed it onto pavements. It was deliberately attention-seeking, we wanted to be shocking and surprise people.

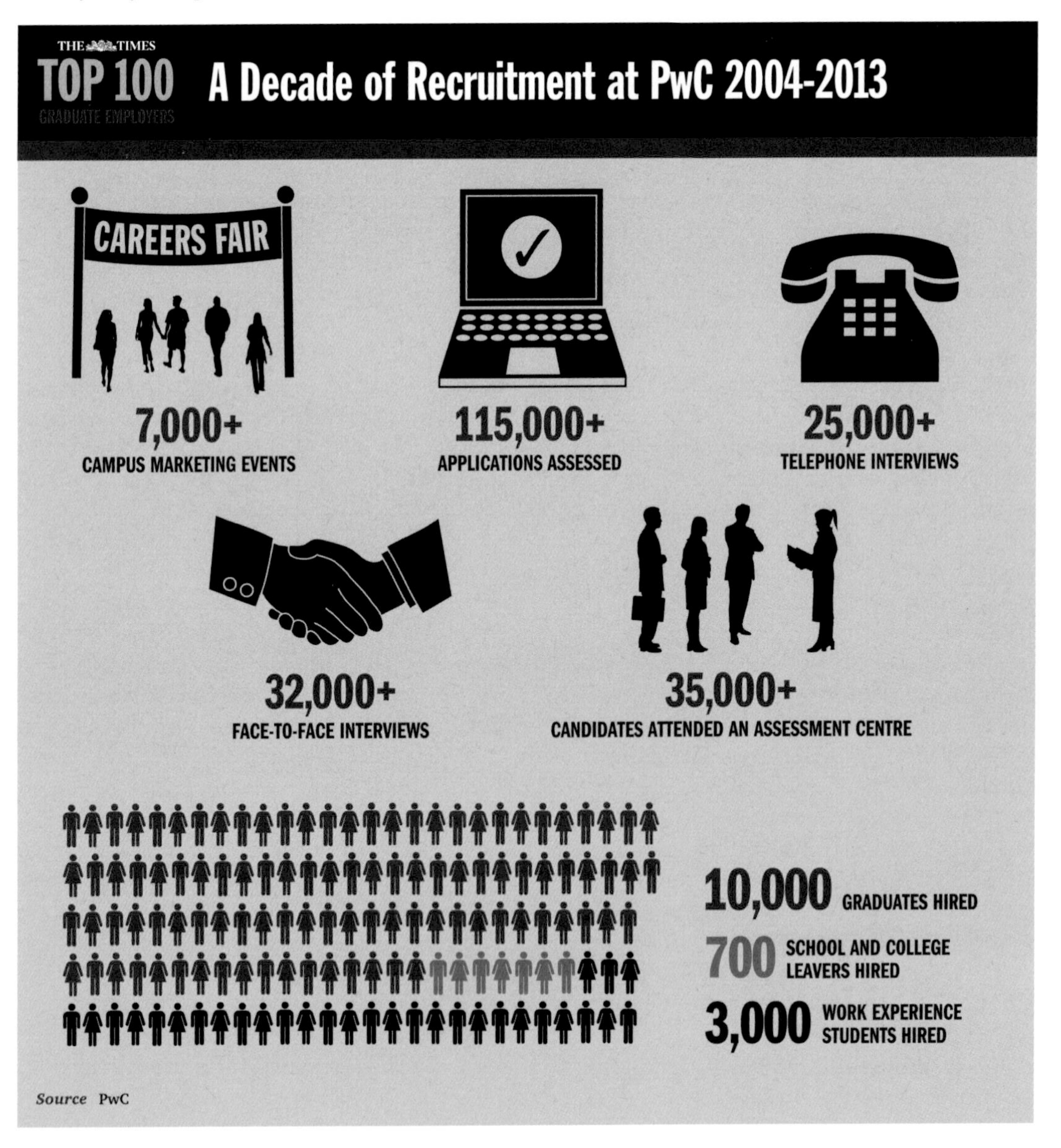

It was so unusual to see an organisation like ours doing these kinds of things on campus that it really helped distinguish us from our competitors – nobody knew what was going to happen next. Our brand had become an experience and this was something we worked hard to replicate through the whole of our graduate recruitment process. Everyone that students met from the firm, the way in which letters were done, the way we communicated with them had to be completely consistent with this really engaging and open-minded approach.

Ten years since first reaching number one, our commitment to recruiting the country's top graduates is as strong as ever. PwC continues to hire over a thousand graduates annually in the UK, as well as recruiting increasing numbers through its school-leaver programmes and taking on experienced accountants and other professionals. Over the last ten years, the firm has grown rapidly, with new businesses and opportunities, which means we've remained one of the country's biggest recruiters of graduates.

Being the top choice for university-leavers has been hugely important to the firm, not just to enable us to recruit the very best brains for the work we do but also to help build the firm for the future. You can't suddenly magic up hundreds of people with a particular skill-set, it takes time to train and develop new graduates to become experienced professionals. Not everyone will choose to stay with us long-term and only around fifty of the thousand graduates that we recruit each year will make it to partner level in the firm. But we know that if people come through PwC with a great experience, they can go off and do something else, becoming advocates for us and our business. We work very hard to make sure the majority leave with a good experience of the firm.

PwC is a very different firm today to the one I originally joined over thirty years ago. The academic standard of our graduates is noticeably higher and in many ways it's much harder work for new recruits than it was. The advent of technology and the pressures on all aspects of the work we do – in terms of speed of delivery and the 24/7 markets we operate in with global clients – means that the skills needed by our people are greater than ever. We're always very careful when we're promoting our graduate opportunities to present a balanced message about life at the firm. We're very clear about the demands, how serious it is and how difficult it can be to succeed in the early years and just how hard it might be.

We're immensely proud to have been number one in *The Times Top 100 Graduate Employers* for the last ten years – it's been an amazing journey for PwC and the ten-thousand graduates we've recruited over that time. Today's university students think of the firm as 'exciting', 'prestigious' and a 'market leader' and last year we attracted over thirty-five thousand applications for our graduate, school-leaver and work experience programmes, an all-time record for the firm.

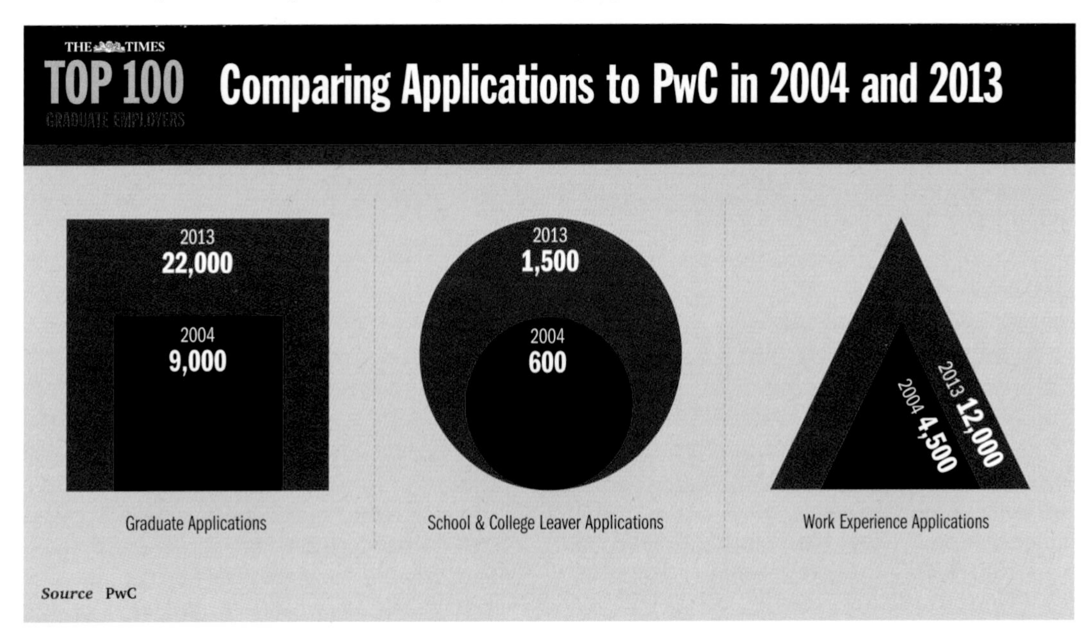

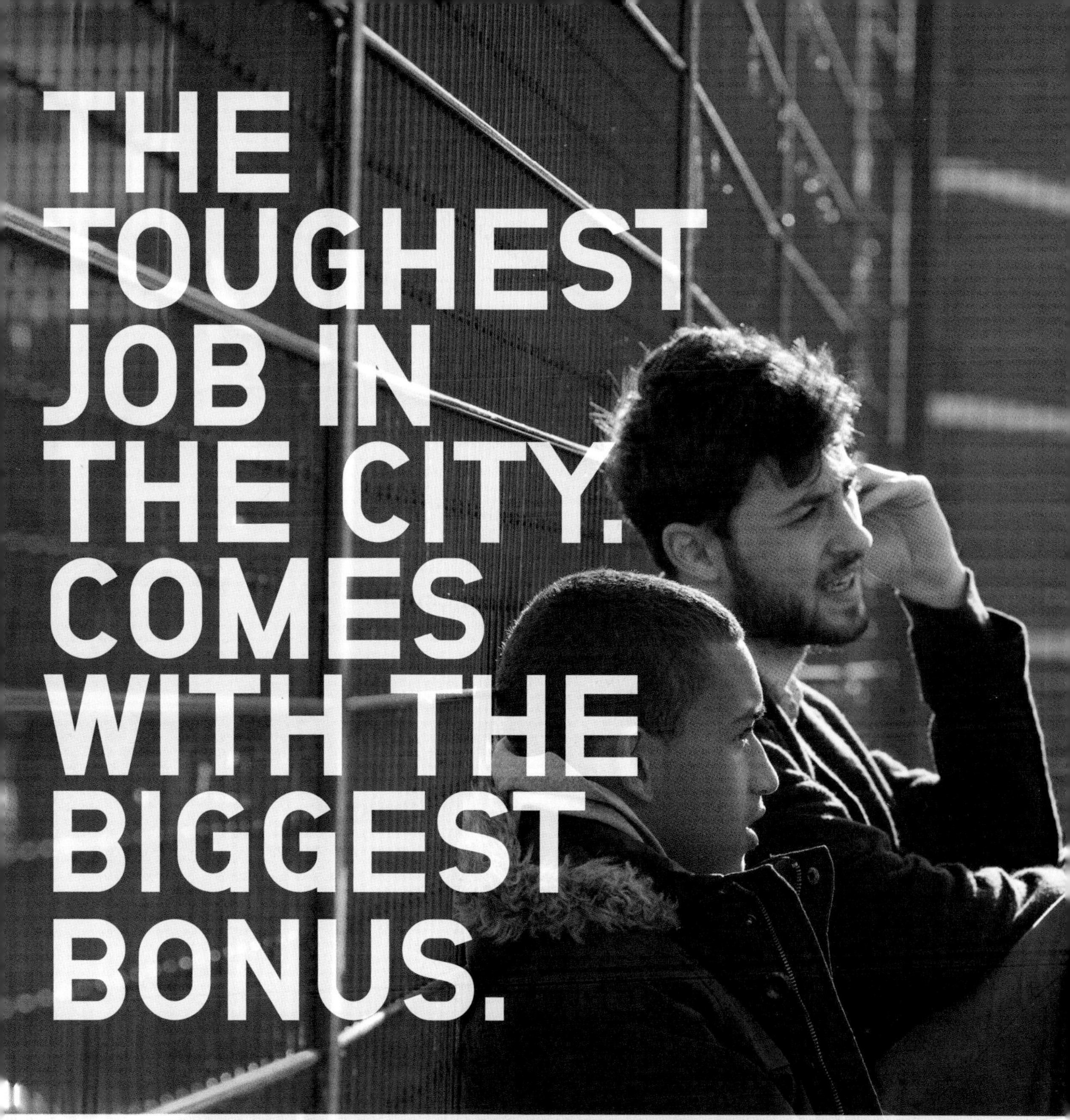
THE
TOUGHEST
JOB IN
THE CITY.
COMES
WITH THE
BIGGEST
BONUS.

Graduate job

See what it takes to make it to the very top of PwC from the perspective of one of our female leaders. Do well and you could get a place on our summer internship, or a graduate job offer.

Students of all years

Work alongside specialists in one of our business areas. You'll work on client projects for six to eight weeks, to give you the best insight into our work. Do well and you could go back to university with a graduate job offer.

Penultimate year students

Develop business skills by working on client projects. In 11 months you'll have gained a deep insight into our business and developed your technical skills. This opportunity is ideal if you need to complete a placement as part of your degree, and could lead to a graduate job offer.

Sandwich/placement students

THE TIMES
TOP 100
GRADUATE EMPLOYERS

Publication Date
SEPTEMBER 1999

The definitive student guide to the leading
recruiting graduates in 1999-2000.

Fifteen Years of Researching Britain's Top Employers

By **Gill Thomas**
Publisher, *The Times Top 100 Graduate Employers*

This is the fifteenth edition of *The Times Top 100 Graduate Employers* – the original directory was published in 1999, revealing for the first time which organisations the UK's top undergraduates aspired to work for after university.

Just as copies of that first edition were being distributed to campuses around the county, the Millennium Dome was preparing to open in London ready for the year 2000 celebrations, eleven European countries introduced the new Euro currency, the Scottish Parliament reconvened in Edinburgh for the first time in almost three hundred years, George W. Bush announced he would run for the US Presidency and Britney Spears had the UK's best-selling single of the year with 'Baby One More Time'.

For new graduates fresh out of university, 1999 wasn't a bad time to be job hunting. Entry-level vacancies had shot up by more than 12 per cent the previous year, one of the largest annual increases since the late 1980s and graduate starting salaries continued to rise at nearly twice the rate of inflation.

Final year students taking part in *The UK Graduate Careers Survey 1999* – the annual survey of finalists' career expectations and aspirations conducted by High Fliers Research – voted Andersen Consulting (then the consulting arm of accounting firm Arthur Andersen) the year's top graduate employer and more finalists applied for jobs in management consulting than any other career area.

"A total of 201 different organisations have now appeared within The Times Top 100 Graduate Employers."

It is interesting to compare the results of that survey with the similar research carried out with the 'Class of 2013' earlier this year. In 1999, almost half of the top twenty employers that students believed offered the best opportunities for graduates were manufacturing or industrial companies. By contrast, just three of the organisations in this year's top twenty actually make anything – the list is dominated instead by accounting & professional services firms, public sector employers and retailers.

This year, typical salaries at a *Top 100* graduate employer are £29,000, an impressive 67% higher than the starting rates for graduates in 1999. The average then was £17,400 and fewer than forty employers offered new recruits packages of £20,000 or more.

Only half of finalists used the internet in 1999 to research their career options but record numbers took part in employer presentations and university careers fairs. During the 2012-2013 recruitment season, although virtually every graduate job hunter relied on employers' websites as a key

Find out more on page 108

source of employment information, attendances at campus events such as fairs, presentations and skills training workshops remain as strong as ever.

Andersen Consulting (now Accenture) is one of just three organisations that has made it to number one since *The Times Top 100 Graduate Employers* directory was first published. The firm held onto the top spot for a further three years after 1999 and their success heralded a huge surge in popularity for careers in consulting. At its peak in 2001, almost one in six graduates applied for jobs in the sector. In the year before the firm changed its name from Andersen Consulting to Accenture, it astutely introduced a new graduate package that included a £28,500 starting salary (a sky-high figure for graduates in 2000) and a much-talked-about £10,000 bonus, helping to assure the firm's popularity, irrespective of its corporate branding.

In 2003, after two dismal years in graduate recruitment when vacancies for university-leavers dropped by more than a fifth following the terrorist attacks of 11th September 2001, the Civil Service was named Britain's leading graduate employer. A year later it was displaced by PricewaterhouseCoopers, the accounting and professional services firm formed from the merger of Price Waterhouse and Coopers & Lybrand in 1998. At the time, the firm was the largest private sector recruiter of graduates, with an intake in 2004 of more than a thousand trainees.

PricewaterhouseCoopers (now known simply as PwC) has remained at number one for a unprecedented ten years running, increasing its share of the student vote from five per cent in 2004 to more than 10 per cent in 2007. The following year, the firm faced its stiffest competition yet from rivals Deloitte and retained the top ranking by just seven votes, but the margin between the firms has increased again since and this year more than four hundred votes separated the two employers.

PwC's reign as the leading employer represents a real renaissance for the entire accounting sector. Whereas fifteen years ago, a career in accountancy was regarded as a safe, traditional employment choice, today's profession is viewed in a very different light. The training required to become a chartered accountant is now seen as a prized business qualification and the sector's leading firms are regularly described as 'dynamic' and 'international' by undergraduates looking for their first job after university. Accountancy's transformation is underlined by the fact that in 1999 just ten per cent of final year students opted for one of the top five accounting firms in the *Top 100*, compared with the 19 per cent of votes polled by the 'Big Four' firms in this year's list.

A total of 201 different organisations have now appeared within *The Times Top 100 Graduate Employers* since its inception and over forty of these have made it into the rankings every year for the last fifteen years. The most consistent performers since 1999 have been PwC, KPMG and the Civil Service, each of which have never been lower than 8th place in the league table. The NHS has also

THE TIMES **TOP 100** GRADUATE EMPLOYERS

Movers & Shakers in the Top 100

HIGHEST NEW ENTRIES		HIGHEST CLIMBING EMPLOYERS	
1999	**PFIZER** (31st)	1999	**SCHLUMBERGER** (UP 13 PLACES)
2000	**MORGAN STANLEY** (34th)	2000	**CAPITAL ONE** (UP 32 PLACES)
2001	**MARCONI** (36th)	2001	**EUROPEAN COMMISSION** (UP 36 PLACES)
2002	**GUINNESS UDV** (44th)	2002	**WPP** (UP 36 PLACES)
2003	**ASDA** (40th)	2003	**ROLLS-ROYCE** (UP 37 PLACES)
2004	**BAKER & MCKENZIE** (61st)	2004	**J.P. MORGAN** (UP 29 PLACES)
2005	**PENGUIN** (70th)	2005	**TEACH FIRST** (UP 22 PLACES)
2006	**FUJITSU** (81st)	2006	**GOOGLE** (UP 32 PLACES)
2007	**BDO STOY HAYWARD** (74th)	2007	**PFIZER** (UP 30 PLACES)
2008	**SKY** (76th)	2008	**CO-OPERATIVE GROUP** (UP 39 PLACES)
2009	**BDO STOY HAYWARD** (68th)	2009	**CADBURY** (UP 48 PLACES)
2010	**SAATCHI & SAATCHI** (49th)	2010	**ASDA** (UP 41 PLACES)
2011	**APPLE** (53rd)	2011	**CENTRICA** (UP 41 PLACES)
2012	**EUROPEAN COMMISSION** (56th)	2012	**NESTLÉ** (UP 44 PLACES)
2013	**SIEMENS** (70th)	2013	**DEPARTMENT FOR INTERNATIONAL DEVELOPMENT** (UP 40 PLACES)

Source High Fliers Research

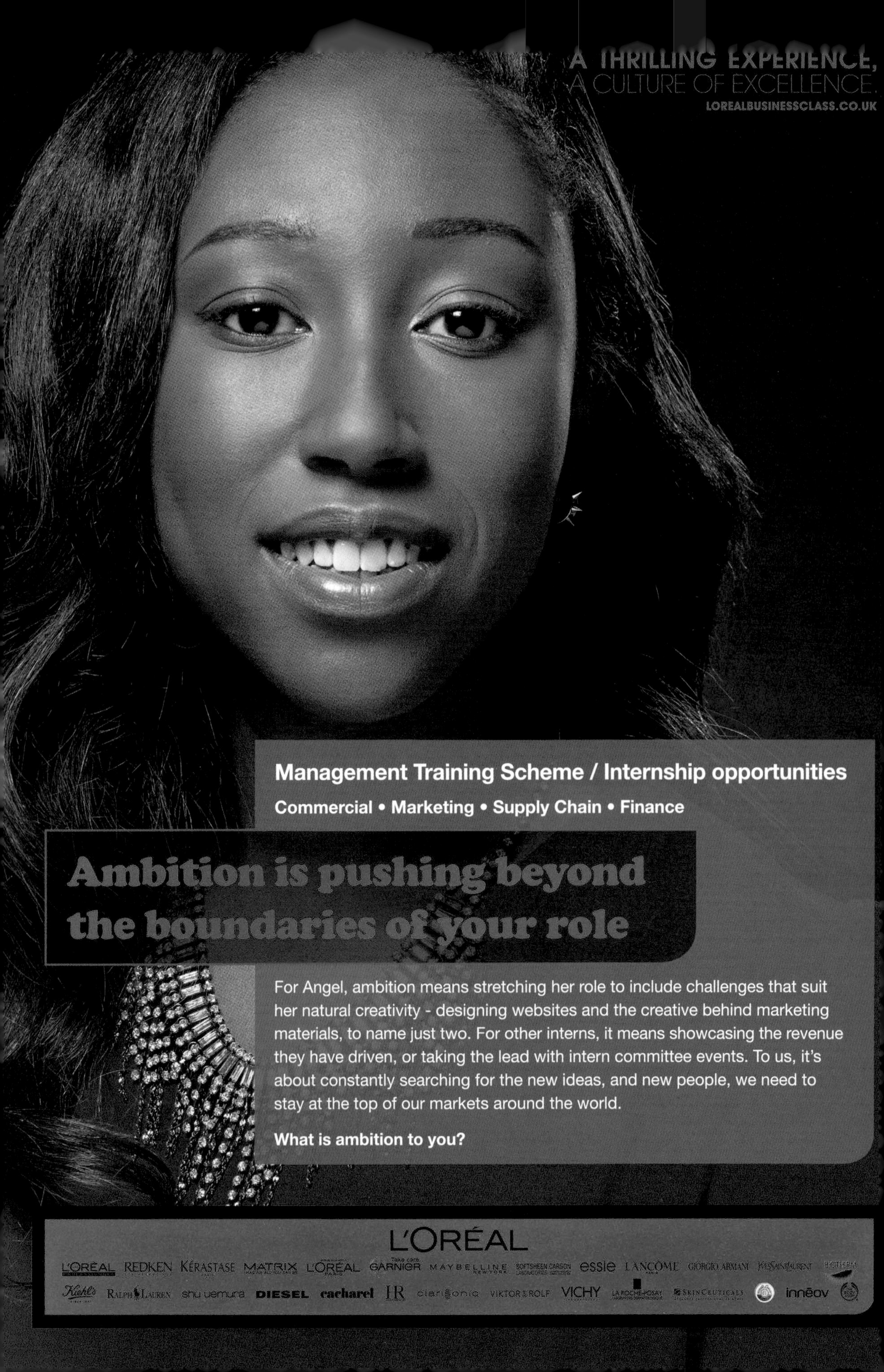

A THRILLING EXPERIENCE,
A CULTURE OF EXCELLENCE.
LOREALBUSINESSCLASS.CO.UK
Management Training Scheme / Internship opportunities
Commercial • Marketing • Supply Chain • Finance
Ambition is pushing beyond the boundaries of your role
For Angel, ambition means stretching her role to include challenges that suit her natural creativity - designing websites and the creative behind marketing materials, to name just two. For other interns, it means showcasing the revenue they have driven, or taking the lead with intern committee events. To us, it's about constantly searching for the new ideas, and new people, we need to stay at the top of our markets around the world.
What is ambition to you?
L'ORÉAL
L'ORÉAL REDKEN KÉRASTASE MATRIX L'ORÉAL GARNIER MAYBELLINE essie LANCÔME GIORGIO ARMANI
Kiehl's RALPH LAUREN shu uemura DIESEL cacharel HR clarisonic VIKTOR&ROLF VICHY LA ROCHE-POSAY SKINCEUTICALS innéov

had a formidable record, appearing in every top ten since 2003, and the BBC, Goldman Sachs and Ernst & Young (now EY) have all remained within the top twenty throughout the last decade.

Google, Jaguar Land Rover, Lidl and Atkins have each climbed more than fifty places within the *Top 100* during the last fifteen years.

Other employers haven't been so successful. British Airways, ranked in 6th place in 1999, dropped out of the *Top 100* altogether in 2010 and 2011. Ford, which was once rated as high as 14th, disappeared out of the list in 2006 after cancelling its graduate recruitment programme two years previously and BT dropped an eye-watering forty-seven places in a single year when it pulled out of its 2009-2010 university recruitment campaign.

Thirty-two employers – including Nokia, the Home Office, Nationwide, United Biscuits, the Met Office and Capgemini – have the dubious record of having only been ranked in the *Top 100* once during the last fifteen years. And Marconi had the unusual distinction of being one of the highest-ever new entries in 36th place in 2001, only to vanish from the list entirely the following year.

One of the most spectacular ascendancies within the *Top 100* has been the rise of Aldi, which joined the list in 65th place in 2002 and rose to 3rd place in 2009, helped in part by its memorable remuneration package for new recruits (currently £40,000 plus an Audi A4 car).

And Teach First has been another runaway success in the *Top 100* rankings. After appearing as a new entry in 63rd place in 2003, the scheme is now in 3rd place and is the UK's largest individual recruiter of graduates, with 1,550 places available on its two-year programme in 2014.

THE TIMES TOP 100 GRADUATE EMPLOYERS

Winners & Losers in the Top 100

MOST CONSISTENT EMPLOYERS 1999-2013	HIGHEST RANKING	LOWEST RANKING
ANDERSEN (FORMERLY ARTHUR ANDERSEN)	2nd (1999-2001)	3rd (2002)
PWC (FORMERLY PRICEWATERHOUSECOOPERS)	1st (2004-2013)	3rd (1999-2001, 2003)
KPMG	3rd (2006-2008, 2011-2012)	8th (1999)
CIVIL SERVICE	1st (2003)	8th (2011)
BBC	5th (2005-2007)	14th (1999)
GLAXOSMITHKLINE	11th (2000)	22nd (2002-2003)
IBM	13th (2000)	24th (2012)
EY (FORMERLY ERNST & YOUNG)	7th (2013)	20th (2001)
ACCENTURE (FORMERLY ANDERSEN CONSULTING)	1st (1999-2002)	16th (2013)
BP	14th (2013)	32nd (2004)
EMPLOYERS CLIMBING HIGHEST 1999-2013	**NEW ENTRY RANKING**	**HIGHEST RANKING**
GOOGLE	85th (2005)	10th (2013)
JAGUAR LAND ROVER	87th (2009)	21st (2013)
MI5 - THE SECURITY SERVICE	96th (2007)	33rd (2010)
ALDI	65th (2002)	3rd (2009)
TEACH FIRST	63rd (2004)	3rd (2013)
LIDL	89th (2009)	31st (2013)
ATKINS	94th (2004)	37th (2009)
ARCADIA GROUP	99th (2001)	47th (2007)
SLAUGHTER AND MAY	90th (2001)	39th (2010)
NESTLÉ	93rd (2009)	43rd (2013)
EMPLOYERS FALLING FURTHEST 1999-2013	**HIGHEST RANKING**	**LOWEST RANKING**
BRITISH AIRWAYS	6th (1999)	Not ranked (2010, 2011)
FORD	11th (1999)	Not ranked (FROM 2006)
THOMSON REUTERS	22nd (2001)	Not ranked (2009-2012)
ASTRAZENECA	24th (2003)	Not ranked (FROM 2012)
MINISTRY OF DEFENCE	35th (2003)	Not ranked (2007, FROM 2012)
MARCONI	36th (2001)	Not ranked (FROM 2002)
DIAGEO	37th (2004)	Not ranked (2008-2009)
ICI	39th (2000)	Not ranked (2001, 2004, FROM 2006)
LOGICA	39th (1999)	Not ranked (FROM 2003)
QINETIQ	43rd (2001)	Not ranked (2007, FROM 2011)

Source High Fliers Research

THE TIMES TOP 100 GRADUATE EMPLOYERS

The Top 10 Graduate Employers 1999-2013

	1999		2004		2009
1.	ANDERSEN CONSULTING	1.	PRICEWATERHOUSECOOPERS	1.	PRICEWATERHOUSECOOPERS
2.	ARTHUR ANDERSEN	2.	CIVIL SERVICE	2.	DELOITTE
3.	PRICEWATERHOUSECOOPERS	3.	ACCENTURE	3.	ALDI
4.	PROCTER & GAMBLE	4.	KPMG	4.	CIVIL SERVICE
5.	GOLDMAN SACHS	5.	NHS	5.	KPMG
6.	CIVIL SERVICE	6.	BBC	6.	NHS
7.	KPMG	7.	ARMY	7.	ACCENTURE
8.	UNILEVER	8.	PROCTER & GAMBLE	8.	TEACH FIRST
9.	ARMY	9.	HSBC	9.	BBC
10.	MARS	10.	DELOITTE (FORMERLY DELOITTE & TOUCHE)	10.	ERNST & YOUNG

	2000		2005		2010
1.	ANDERSEN CONSULTING	1.	PRICEWATERHOUSECOOPERS	1.	PRICEWATERHOUSECOOPERS
2.	PRICEWATERHOUSECOOPERS	2.	CIVIL SERVICE	2.	DELOITTE
3.	ARTHUR ANDERSEN	3.	ACCENTURE	3.	CIVIL SERVICE
4.	CIVIL SERVICE	4.	KPMG	4.	KPMG
5.	ARMY	5.	BBC	5.	ALDI
6.	KPMG	6.	DELOITTE	6.	NHS
7.	UNILEVER	7.	NHS	7.	TEACH FIRST
8.	PROCTER & GAMBLE	8.	HSBC	8.	ACCENTURE
9.	GOLDMAN SACHS	9.	GOLDMAN SACHS	9.	BBC
10.	MARS	10.	PROCTER & GAMBLE	10.	ERNST & YOUNG

	2001		2006		2011
1.	ACCENTURE (FORMERLY ANDERSEN CONSULTING)	1.	PRICEWATERHOUSECOOPERS	1.	PWC (FORMERLY PRICEWATERHOUSECOOPERS)
2.	ANDERSEN (FORMERLY ARTHUR ANDERSEN)	2.	DELOITTE	2.	DELOITTE
3.	PRICEWATERHOUSECOOPERS	3.	KPMG	3.	KPMG
4.	PROCTER & GAMBLE	4.	CIVIL SERVICE	4.	ALDI
5.	GOLDMAN SACHS	5.	BBC	5.	NHS
6.	CIVIL SERVICE	6.	NHS	6.	BBC
7.	KPMG	7.	HSBC	7.	TEACH FIRST
8.	UNILEVER	8.	ACCENTURE	8.	CIVIL SERVICE
9.	ARMY	9.	PROCTER & GAMBLE	9.	ACCENTURE
10.	MARS	10.	GOLDMAN SACHS	10.	ERNST & YOUNG

	2002		2007		2012
1.	ACCENTURE	1.	PRICEWATERHOUSECOOPERS	1.	PWC
2.	PRICEWATERHOUSECOOPERS	2.	DELOITTE	2.	DELOITTE
3.	ANDERSEN	3.	KPMG	3.	KPMG
4.	CIVIL SERVICE	4.	CIVIL SERVICE	4.	TEACH FIRST
5.	ARMY	5.	BBC	5.	ALDI
6.	KPMG	6.	NHS	6.	NHS
7.	UNILEVER	7.	ACCENTURE	7.	CIVIL SERVICE
8.	PROCTER & GAMBLE	8.	HSBC	8.	ERNST & YOUNG
9.	GOLDMAN SACHS	9.	ALDI	9.	BBC
10.	MARS	10.	GOLDMAN SACHS	10.	JOHN LEWIS PARTNERSHIP

	2003		2008		2013
1.	CIVIL SERVICE	1.	PRICEWATERHOUSECOOPERS	1.	PWC
2.	ACCENTURE	2.	DELOITTE	2.	DELOITTE
3.	PRICEWATERHOUSECOOPERS	3.	KPMG	3.	TEACH FIRST
4.	ARMY	4.	ACCENTURE	4.	KPMG
5.	KPMG	5.	NHS	5.	CIVIL SERVICE
6.	HSBC	6.	CIVIL SERVICE	6.	ALDI
7.	BBC	7.	BBC	7.	EY (FORMERLY ERNST & YOUNG)
8.	PROCTER & GAMBLE	8.	ALDI	8.	NHS
9.	NHS	9.	TEACH FIRST	9.	JOHN LEWIS PARTNERSHIP
10.	DELOITTE & TOUCHE	10.	GOLDMAN SACHS	10.	GOOGLE

Source High Fliers Research

THE TIMES

TOP 100

GRADUATE EMPLOYERS

Index

EMPLOYER	TOP 100 RANKING	GRADUATE VACANCIES IN 2014																	NUMBER OF VACANCIES	PAGE
		ACCOUNTANCY	CONSULTING	ENGINEERING	FINANCE	GENERAL MANAGEMENT	HUMAN RESOURCES	INVESTMENT BANKING	IT	LAW	LOGISTICS	MARKETING	MEDIA	PROPERTY	PURCHASING	RESEARCH & DEVELOPMENT	RETAILING	SALES		
ACCENTURE	16		●						●										450	58
AIRBUS	90			●	●		●		●		●				●	●			50-60	60
ALDI	6					●											●		140	62
ALLEN & OVERY	34									●									90	64
ARCADIA GROUP	75				●						●				●		●		Around 250	66
ARMY	26			●					●	●	●								650	68
ARUP	39		●	●	●	●										●			150+	70
ASDA	48				●		●		●		●	●		●	●		●		Around 80	72
ATKINS	61		●	●					●					●					300+	74
BAKER & MCKENZIE	72									●									34	76
BALFOUR BEATTY	93		●	●	●	●	●		●			●							150	78
BANK OF AMERICA MERRILL LYNCH	66				●		●	●	●										200+	80
BARCLAYS	12	●			●	●	●	●	●			●							250+	82
BBC	11			●			●		●				●			●			200	84
BLACKROCK	92				●				●			●						●	90	86
BOOTS	55				●				●			●			●		●		50	88
BOSTON CONSULTING GROUP	54		●																No fixed quota	90
BP	14	●		●	●	●	●	●	●		●				●	●	●	●	220	92
BRITISH AIRWAYS	56		●	●	●	●	●		●		●				●	●			Up to 70	94
BT	60		●	●		●	●		●	●		●				●		●	Around 200	96
CANCER RESEARCH UK	49				●	●	●		●			●				●	●		6	98
CENTRICA	98			●	●	●	●		●			●							60+	100
CHANNEL 4	76											●	●			●		●	2-4	102
CITI	46				●		●	●	●										200	104
CIVIL SERVICE FAST STREAM	5			●		●	●		●										800+	106
CLIFFORD CHANCE	36									●									100	108
CO-OPERATIVE GROUP	74																●		To be confirmed	110
COCA-COLA ENTERPRISES	81			●	●		●					●						●	20+	112
CREDIT SUISSE	62							●											No fixed quota	114
DANONE	91				●		●				●	●				●		●	25-30	116
DELOITTE	2	●	●		●				●					●					1,200	118
DFID	59			●	●	●	●		●						●	●			50	120
DIAGEO	82			●	●		●					●						●	50	122
DLA PIPER	64									●									80	124
EDF ENERGY	79			●	●		●					●							60	126
EUROPEAN COMMISSION (EU CAREERS)	58				●	●	●		●	●		●	●			●			No fixed quota	128
EY	7	●	●		●				●										700	130
FRESHFIELDS BRUCKHAUS DERINGER	45									●									90	132
GE	83	●		●	●		●		●			●						●	50	134
GLAXOSMITHKLINE	19			●	●		●		●			●				●		●	50+	136
GOLDMAN SACHS	18	●			●		●	●	●										300	138
GOOGLE	10		●	●			●		●			●	●					●	No fixed quota	140
GRANT THORNTON	86	●																	300+	142
HERBERT SMITH FREEHILLS	78									●									70	144
HOGAN LOVELLS	68									●									Up to 60	146
IBM	20		●						●									●	300+	148

EMPLOYER	TOP 100 RANKING	ACCOUNTANCY	CONSULTING	ENGINEERING	FINANCE	GENERAL MANAGEMENT	HUMAN RESOURCES	INVESTMENT BANKING	IT	LAW	LOGISTICS	MARKETING	MEDIA	PROPERTY	PURCHASING	RESEARCH & DEVELOPMENT	RETAILING	SALES	NUMBER OF VACANCIES	PAGE
		GRADUATE VACANCIES IN 2014																		
JAGUAR LAND ROVER	21	●		●	●		●		●		●	●		●	●	●	●		250	150
JOHN LEWIS PARTNERSHIP	9				●	●			●						●		●		65	152
KPMG	4	●	●		●		●		●										800+	154
L'ORÉAL	28				●						●	●						●	35	156
LIDL	31					●								●	●		●	●	30	158
LINKLATERS	42									●									110	160
LLOYD'S	87				●														25	162
LLOYDS BANKING GROUP	33				●	●	●	●	●										Around 200	164
MARKS & SPENCER	32					●	●		●		●	●			●	●	●		200	166
MARS	52			●	●	●						●			●	●		●	35	168
MCDONALD'S	47					●													400	170
MCKINSEY & COMPANY	30		●																No fixed quota	172
METROPOLITAN POLICE	63																		To be confirmed	174
MI5	51					●			●										50+	176
MICROSOFT	27		●						●									●	40	178
MONDELĒZ INTERNATIONAL	96			●	●		●				●	●				●		●	Around 20	180
MORGAN STANLEY	38				●		●	●	●										No fixed quota	182
MORRISONS	84				●	●	●		●		●	●		●			●		Around 100	184
NATIONAL GRID	100	●		●	●	●			●		●				●	●			30+	186
NESTLÉ	43			●	●		●		●			●						●	50	188
NETWORK RAIL	95	●		●	●	●			●		●			●	●				120-140	190
NEWTON EUROPE	94		●						●										40-50	192
NGDP	65					●													50+	194
NHS	8				●	●	●		●										Around 300	196
OXFAM	85	●					●		●			●	●			●	●		50+ (voluntary)	198
PENGUIN	67	●			●		●		●	●	●	●	●		●			●	30-50	200
PROCTER & GAMBLE	23	●		●	●		●		●		●	●				●		●	100	202
PWC	1	●	●		●				●	●									1,200	204
ROLLS-ROYCE	24			●	●	●	●								●			●	Around 400	206
ROYAL AIR FORCE	89			●		●	●		●		●								No fixed quota	208
ROYAL BANK OF SCOTLAND GROUP	25	●			●	●	●	●	●			●							350+	210
ROYAL NAVY	88			●	●	●	●		●	●	●					●			No fixed quota	212
SAINSBURY'S	37						●				●	●			●		●		30	214
SANTANDER	77				●	●	●										●		50-75	216
SHELL	29		●	●	●		●		●		●	●			●	●	●	●	Around 130	218
SIEMENS	70			●	●	●			●						●			●	80+	220
SKY	35	●		●	●	●	●		●			●	●						80+	222
SLAUGHTER AND MAY	44									●									75-80	224
TEACH FIRST	3	●	●	●	●	●	●	●	●	●	●	●	●	●	●	●	●	●	1,550	226
TESCO	15				●	●	●		●		●	●		●	●	●	●		100+	228
THOMSON REUTERS	97	●			●				●				●						30-50	230
TRANSPORT FOR LONDON	99	●		●	●	●			●		●	●		●	●				130	232
UBS	80							●											100+	234
UNILEVER	13			●	●		●		●		●	●				●		●	60-70	236
WPP	50											●	●						1-10	238

accenture.com/ukgraduates

facebook.com/AccentureUK  grad.apps@accenture.com 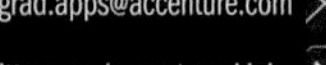

youtube.com/AccentureUKcareers  twitter.com/accentureukjobs 

Accenture is a world-leading management consulting, technology services and outsourcing company that's transforming the way many of the biggest organisations do business. Accenture is the perfect choice for a career that will challenge and inspire.

Through state-of-the-art thinking, deep technological expertise and close collaboration, Accenture helps organisations in every sector achieve even higher performance. How? By spotting opportunities and delivering innovative solutions that not only add value, but also enable clients to evolve to the next level.

Accenture's influence reaches far and wide, changing the way organisations perform, and impacting how the world interacts with technology. For instance, 41 million internet searches are enabled by Accenture every hour – while some 90 million packages around the world are processed by our systems every day.

It's not just clients who are benefiting from Accenture's expertise. High-performing graduates who join Accenture can expect to sharpen their skills as they enjoy direct involvement with a broad spectrum of clients. Whether they're looking to specialise as a Consultant or a Technologist, new starters will be immersed in live projects – while a structured programme of mentoring and learning will help them evolve beyond their imagination. The encouragement and opportunities for personal and professional development are truly exceptional at Accenture.

Graduate opportunities are available across Consulting and Technology Solutions. For Consulting, a 2:1 in any discipline is welcome; for Technology Solutions, applicants will need a 2:1 in a technology, maths, science or engineering-related degree – and both require a genuine passion for technology.

GRADUATE VACANCIES IN 2014

CONSULTING

IT

NUMBER OF VACANCIES

450 graduate jobs

LOCATIONS OF VACANCIES

STARTING SALARY FOR 2014

Up to £31,500

Plus a £10,000 sign-on bonus for Consulting roles.

UNIVERSITY VISITS IN 2013-14

ASTON, BATH, BRISTOL, BRUNEL, CAMBRIDGE, DURHAM, EDINBURGH, EXETER, IMPERIAL COLLEGE LONDON, KING'S COLLEGE LONDON, KENT, LEEDS, LONDON SCHOOL OF ECONOMICS, LOUGHBOROUGH, MANCHESTER, NEWCASTLE, NOTTINGHAM, OXFORD, SOUTHAMPTON, ST ANDREWS, SURREY, UNIVERSITY COLLEGE LONDON, WARWICK

Please check with your university careers service for full details of local events.

MINIMUM ENTRY REQUIREMENTS

2.1 Degree

APPLICATION DEADLINE

Year-round recruitment

FURTHER INFORMATION

www.Top100GraduateEmployers.com

Register now for the latest news, events information and graduate recruitment details for Britain's leading employers.

AIRBUS
AN EADS COMPANY

www.airbus.com/work

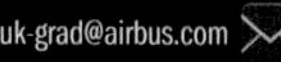
airbusuk-grad@airbus.com

twitter.com/airbus facebook.com/airbuscareers

youtube.com/airbus linkedin.com/company/airbus/careers

GRADUATE VACANCIES IN 2014
- ENGINEERING
- FINANCE
- HUMAN RESOURCES
- IT
- LOGISTICS
- PURCHASING
- RESEARCH & DEVELOPMENT

NUMBER OF VACANCIES
50-60 graduate jobs

LOCATIONS OF VACANCIES

STARTING SALARY FOR 2014
£25,000+
Plus welcome payment.

UNIVERSITY VISITS IN 2013-14
BATH, BELFAST, BIRMINGHAM, BRISTOL, CAMBRIDGE, IMPERIAL COLLEGE LONDON, LIVERPOOL, LOUGHBOROUGH, MANCHESTER, NOTTINGHAM, SHEFFIELD, SOUTHAMPTON, STRATHCLYDE
Please check with your university careers service for full details of local events.

MINIMUM ENTRY REQUIREMENTS
2.1 Degree

APPLICATION DEADLINE
29th November 2013

FURTHER INFORMATION
www.Top100GraduateEmployers.com
Register now for the latest news, events information and graduate recruitment details for Britain's leading employers.

Airbus is a leading aircraft manufacturer with the most modern and comprehensive family of airliners on the market. Over 12,800 Airbus aircraft have been sold to more than 350 customers worldwide and more than 7,870 of these have been delivered since the company first entered the market in the early seventies.

Airbus aircraft range in capacity from 100 to more than 500 seats: the single-aisle A320 Family, including A320neo, best selling aircraft in aviation history, the wide-body long-range A330 Family including the freighter and MRTT, the double-deck A380 Family and the all-new, next generation A350 XWB Family.

To stay on top, Airbus needs dynamic graduates and talented undergraduates whose skills and potential are fully maximised. A vast range of career development opportunities are provided, including personal development strategies and training courses to enable each individual to plan their future career with the company.

Innovative graduates will enjoy the chance to develop their technical and leadership skills on the Airbus Direct Entry Graduate (DEG) Programme. A detailed knowledge of business functions will be gained through placements in the UK and Europe, with strategic partners, customers and suppliers. Involvement in education and community projects, to broaden personal and management skills, is also part of the programme.

For graduates looking for direct roles, Airbus has vacancies throughout the year in various disciplines in France, Germany, Spain and the UK.

At Airbus work-life balance through flexible working is actively promoted. Individuality is encouraged and diversity embraced. Airbus wants people to bring their own style and contribute to the richness of the organisation.

your future
by Airbus
AIRBUS
concept plane

You
Tube

in

f

AIRBUS

As one of the world's leading retailers, Aldi is renowned for attracting top quality, ambitious graduates who have a determination to succeed. In return for an excellent remuneration package, Aldi offers graduates real responsibility from day one.

Only the very best candidates are selected, and their ability to inspire, lead and motivate in the fast-paced environment which has made Aldi a driving force in retail is a vital prerequisite for all of the company's managers.

Aldi Area Managers must be team players – the business actively seeks out graduates who can demonstrate leadership qualities, either in their academic or personal lives. The initiative and skills required to lead a local or university team, undertake voluntary work, or strive for personal excellence are favoured over first-class honours. Aldi is looking for self-starters who can inspire others within a retail environment and have a desire to succeed within one of the UK's fastest growing companies.

Candidates who are selected for Aldi's Area Management Programme begin their journey in-store and within weeks will be managing one store of their own. Excellence and attention to detail are expected throughout the role, and in return, Aldi offers fast-track career progression and real responsibility.

After receiving thorough training in all aspects of retail management, from store operations through to financial administration, Aldi's graduate trainees are given the skills to take charge of a multi-million pound area of 3 to 4 stores to run, as and when they are ready.

To be successful, graduates will need good academics, high energy levels, a willingness to learn and the determination to overcome the challenges ahead. In return, Aldi offers an excellent starting salary and a fully expensed Audi A4.

GRADUATE VACANCIES IN 2014

GENERAL MANAGEMENT

RETAILING

NUMBER OF VACANCIES

140 graduate jobs

LOCATIONS OF VACANCIES

STARTING SALARY FOR 2014

£40,000

UNIVERSITY VISITS IN 2013-14

ABERDEEN, ASTON, BATH, BIRMINGHAM, CARDIFF, DUNDEE, DURHAM, EAST ANGLIA, EDINBURGH, ESSEX, EXETER, GLASGOW, LANCASTER, LEEDS, LEICESTER, LIVERPOOL, LOUGHBOROUGH, MANCHESTER, NEWCASTLE, NOTTINGHAM, SHEFFIELD, STRATHCLYDE, WARWICK, YORK

Please check with your university careers service for full details of local events.

MINIMUM ENTRY REQUIREMENTS

2.1 Degree

APPLICATION DEADLINE

Year-round recruitment

FURTHER INFORMATION

www.Top100GraduateEmployers.com

Register now for the latest news, events information and graduate recruitment details for Britain's leading employers.

ALLEN & OVERY

www.aograduate.com

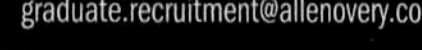

twitter.com/allenoverygrads  facebook.com/AllenOveryGrads

Allen & Overy is a pioneering legal practice operating around the world at the frontline of developing business. By helping companies, institutions and governments tackle ever more complex issues and transactions on a global stage, it is leading the way and extending what is possible in law.

With 42 offices in 29 countries, plus a network of relationship firms in other locations, Allen & Overy is one of the few legal practices that can genuinely claim to be global, covering 99% of the world's economy.

For the firm's clients this means global reach and access to high-calibre, local expertise, while for trainees, it means exposure to international work, collaboration with colleagues in other offices and, in many cases, the opportunity to travel. In 2012, 69% of its transactional work involved two or more countries, 47% involved three or more, and 22% involved five or more.

Trainee lawyers joining the firm enter an environment characterised by advanced thinking and a global outlook. They are exposed to challenging and meaningful work from the outset, supporting a partner or senior associate in each of their training 'seats'. In addition, they are encouraged to spend six months in one of the firm's overseas offices, or on secondment to one of its corporate clients – currently around 80% of its trainees take up this opportunity.

Alongside a rich and exciting experience as a trainee, graduates can also look forward to working in a uniquely open and supportive culture. Allen & Overy has established a reputation for combining the very highest professional standards with warmth and approachability.

Regardless of their degree discipline – and around half of the firm's trainees studied subjects other than law – joining Allen & Overy puts graduates at the forefront of the rapidly-evolving global market for legal services.

GRADUATE VACANCIES IN 2014

LAW

NUMBER OF VACANCIES

90 graduate jobs

For training contracts starting in 2016.

LOCATIONS OF VACANCIES

STARTING SALARY FOR 2014

£39,000

UNIVERSITY VISITS IN 2013-14

BATH, BELFAST, BIRMINGHAM, BRISTOL, CAMBRIDGE, CARDIFF, CITY, DURHAM, EDINBURGH, EXETER, GLASGOW, IMPERIAL COLLEGE LONDON, KING'S COLLEGE LONDON, LANCASTER, LEEDS, LEICESTER, LIVERPOOL, LONDON SCHOOL OF ECONOMICS, LOUGHBOROUGH, MANCHESTER, NEWCASTLE, NORTHUMBRIA, NOTTINGHAM, OXFORD, QUEEN MARY LONDON, READING, ROYAL HOLLOWAY LONDON, SCHOOL OF AFRICAN STUDIES, SHEFFIELD, SOUTHAMPTON, ST ANDREWS, STRATHCLYDE, TRINITY COLLEGE DUBLIN, ULSTER, UNIVERSITY COLLEGE DUBLIN, UNIVERSITY COLLEGE LONDON, WARWICK, YORK

Please check with your university careers service for full details of local events.

MINIMUM ENTRY REQUIREMENTS

2.1 Degree

340 UCAS points

APPLICATION DEADLINE

Law: 31st July 2014

Non-law: 14th January 2014

FURTHER INFORMATION

www.Top100GraduateEmployers.com

Register now for the latest news, events information and graduate recruitment details for Britain's leading employers.

Arcadia

www.arcadiagroup.co.uk/careers

group.resourcing@arcadiagroup.co.uk

twitter.com/Arcadia_Talent facebook.com/ArcadiaFutureTalent 

Arcadia Group is the UK's largest privately owned fashion retailer with over 43,000 employees. Arcadia's portfolio includes nine of the high street's best known brands – BHS, Burton, Dorothy Perkins, Evans, Miss Selfridge, Outfit, Topshop, Topman and Wallis.

Arcadia's graduate recruits provide invaluable support to the business in Buying and Merchandising roles, as well as Group roles such as Finance and E-commerce. Successful graduates come from a variety of degree backgrounds and benefit from direct, on-the-job training that ensures they are provided with real skills and responsibilities from day one.

By providing them with the tools to manage their own careers, and encouraging them to move between the nine brands and Group Functions, Arcadia is known for having one of the most experienced and rounded workforces in the industry.

Arcadia recruits all year round and looks for self starters who can bring something new to the fast-paced business. In return graduates are offered a breadth of opportunities and the scope to develop their career in the knowledge that they are working for one of the most inspirational fashion retailers in the industry.

After the initial online application, graduates will be invited to a video interview and those who are successful will then participate in a face-to-face assessment centre, followed by a brand/department interview.

Graduates are rewarded with a competitive salary, up to 25 days holiday, discretionary bonus, membership to the group pension scheme, sponsorship of relevant professional qualifications, up to 25% discount on all Arcadia Brands and of course entry into the much coveted sample sales.

GRADUATE VACANCIES IN 2014

- FINANCE
- LOGISTICS
- PURCHASING
- RETAILING

NUMBER OF VACANCIES

Around 250 graduate jobs

LOCATIONS OF VACANCIES

STARTING SALARY FOR 2014

£19,000

UNIVERSITY VISITS IN 2013-14

BIRMINGHAM, KENT, LEEDS, MANCHESTER, NORTHUMBRIA, NOTTINGHAM, NOTTINGHAM TRENT, OXFORD BROOKES, SHEFFIELD, UNIVERSITY COLLEGE LONDON

Please check with your university careers service for full details of local events.

MINIMUM ENTRY REQUIREMENTS

Relevant degree required for some roles.

APPLICATION DEADLINE

Year-round recruitment

FURTHER INFORMATION

www.Top100GraduateEmployers.com

Register now for the latest news, events information and graduate recruitment details for Britain's leading employers.

www.army.mod.uk/join/officer

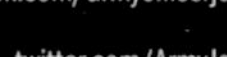
facebook.com/armyofficerjobs

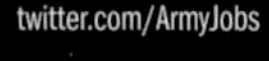
youtube.com/user/ARMYjobs twitter.com/ArmyJobs

Whether it's commanding a platoon of 30 soldiers on a training exercise in Canada or organizing an adventurous training expedition in Arizona, life for graduates as an officer in the British Army is far from routine. This year, the Army has over 700 regular officer and 400 territorial vacancies.

Officer cadets spend 44 weeks at the Royal Military Academy Sandhurst being taught all aspects of soldiering as well as transferable leadership, management and communication skills, in a high-pressure environment. After graduating from Sandhurst, they join their chosen Regiment or Corps for further specialist training, before taking command of around 30 soldiers.

Officer cadets are paid a starting salary of £24,971 while at Sandhurst and this rises to £30,014 on completion of training. Officers can then expect to reach the rank of Captain in 3 years which sees pay increase to £38,463 with annual rises to follow. They also benefit from free health and dental care, subsidised accommodation and food, and a competitive pension.

The Army is one of the largest, most respected graduate employers and offers unrivalled training and development. As well as offering excitement and adventure, the Army supports its officers with continuous professional learning opportunities to further boost their CVs. The Army is looking for people with leadership potential, a strong sense of moral direction and the resourcefulness to succeed.

Those graduates attracted to the idea of becoming an Army officer in their spare time should consider joining the Territorial Army. The experience gained will be invaluable and they'll get paid for the time spent training – with a bonus payment for completing a certain amount of training days each year. For eligibility, search 'Army officer'.

GRADUATE VACANCIES IN 2014

- ENGINEERING
- IT
- LAW
- LOGISTICS

NUMBER OF VACANCIES
650 graduate jobs

LOCATIONS OF VACANCIES

Vacancies also available elsewhere in the world.

STARTING SALARY FOR 2014
£24,971

UNIVERSITY VISITS IN 2013-14
ABERDEEN, BATH, BIRMINGHAM, BRISTOL, CARDIFF, CITY, DUNDEE, DURHAM, EAST ANGLIA, EDINBURGH, LEEDS, LEICESTER, LIVERPOOL, LOUGHBOROUGH, MANCHESTER, NEWCASTLE, NOTTINGHAM, OXFORD, SHEFFIELD, SOUTHAMPTON, UNIVERSITY COLLEGE LONDON
Please check with your university careers service for full details of local events.

MINIMUM ENTRY REQUIREMENTS
240 UCAS points

APPLICATION DEADLINE
Year-round recruitment

FURTHER INFORMATION
www.Top100GraduateEmployers.com
Register now for the latest news, events information and graduate recruitment details for Britain's leading employers.

KEEPING LIFT DOOR OPEN
MALFUNCTIONING VENDING MACHINE
KICKING FILING CABINET

TRAINING FOR OPERATIONS
KENYA
EXPEDITION LEADER
ARIZONA
PARACHUTE JUMP
BRIZE NORTON

ARMY
BE THE BEST

www.arup.com/careers

uk.recruitment@arup.com

twitter.com/arupjobs facebook.com/ArupGroup

youtube.com/user/arupgroup linkedin.com/company/arup

An independent firm offering a broad range of professional services, Arup believes that by bringing great people together, great things will happen. With experts in design, engineering, planning, business consultancy, project management and much more, Arup people work together to shape a better world.

Arup has offices in more than 30 countries across the world, making international team-working part of everyday life and bringing together professionals from diverse disciplines and with complementary skills on a uniquely global scale.

The firm is owned in trust for Arup's employees and this independence translates through the thoughts and actions of its people. Operating principles and commitment to sustainability are paramount and Arup strives not only to embrace this in projects, but also to embed it into everyday thinking and working.

Graduate opportunities span a wide range of disciplines and offer exceptional experience for future leaders who are ambitious, organised and have outstanding communication skills. Arup's diversity helps to foster the creativity that is its hallmark; and the support and freedom for innovation that is encouraged has made Arup the driving force behind some of the most iconic and sustainable designs in the world.

Arup offers competitive benefits and continuous professional development built around employees and their ambitions. Graduates can undertake a professional training programme, accredited by leading organisations such as the Institution of Civil Engineers and the Association for Project Management.

As a firm, Arup seeks exceptional people with fresh ideas and curious minds who want to make a real difference to the environment we live in; passion, drive and creativity are a must.

GRADUATE VACANCIES IN 2014

CONSULTING
ENGINEERING
FINANCE
GENERAL MANAGEMENT
RESEARCH & DEVELOPMENT

NUMBER OF VACANCIES
150+ graduate jobs

LOCATIONS OF VACANCIES

Vacancies also available in Europe, Asia, the USA and elsewhere in the world.

STARTING SALARY FOR 2014
£21,000-£26,000
Plus up to a £4,000 welcome bonus and a bi-annual profit share scheme.

UNIVERSITY VISITS IN 2013-14
BATH, BELFAST, BIRMINGHAM, BRISTOL, CAMBRIDGE, CARDIFF, DUNDEE, DURHAM, EDINBURGH, EXETER, GLASGOW, HERIOT-WATT, IMPERIAL COLLEGE LONDON, LEEDS, LIVERPOOL, LOUGHBOROUGH, MANCHESTER, NEWCASTLE, NOTTINGHAM, OXFORD, SHEFFIELD, SOUTHAMPTON, STRATHCLYDE, SWANSEA, ULSTER, UNIVERSITY COLLEGE LONDON, WARWICK
Please check with your university careers service for full details of local events.

MINIMUM ENTRY REQUIREMENTS
2.1 Degree

APPLICATION DEADLINE
Varies by function

FURTHER INFORMATION
www.Top100GraduateEmployers.com
Register now for the latest news, events information and graduate recruitment details for Britain's leading employers.

ASDA

www.ASDA.jobs/graduates

"It's a real benefit to be part of such a global power as Walmart especially in terms of the economies of scale, collective brain power and best practice."

SANJAY KAPOOR
BUYING MANAGER

Asda is a multi-billion pound business with up to 200,000 colleagues working in over 500 stores and 24 depots. Part of the wider Walmart Group, the world's largest retailer, the organisation is an impressively large graduate employer in the UK with a highly successful Graduate Programme.

Added to this, Asda offers apprenticeships, placements, direct entry roles and more graduate opportunities through George.

In tough economic times, many companies task their graduates with making millions for their shareholders, while their customers continue to struggle. Asda's mission is different – to help its 19 million customers save money every day, by striving to constantly drive down cost. Pennies make pounds, and pounds saved make loyal, happy customers.

Asda has a proven record of developing outstanding business leaders, achieved through a culture where 'Every Day Matters' – where every day is seen as a development opportunity and where every individual colleague counts. To succeed as part of the Graduate Programme, applicants need high levels of strategic and analytical drive, combined with a bright, pro-active approach and an entrepreneurial spirit.

Asda's Graduate Programmes are all designed to give unrivalled exposure and cover Retail Management, Customer Service, Store Development, Logistics Services, Trading (Buying), Finance, HR, IT, Ecommerce (Multichannel), Supply and Marketing.

In return for saving customers money every day, high performers can look forward to responsibility from day one, along with the prospect of being fast-tracked through a business where graduates are developed into future leaders, within Asda and beyond.

GRADUATE VACANCIES IN 2014
- FINANCE
- HUMAN RESOURCES
- IT
- LOGISTICS
- MARKETING
- PROPERTY
- PURCHASING
- RETAILING

NUMBER OF VACANCIES
Around 80 graduate jobs

LOCATIONS OF VACANCIES

STARTING SALARY FOR 2014
£Competitive
Plus benefits.

UNIVERSITY VISITS IN 2013-14
ASTON, BATH, BELFAST, BIRMINGHAM, BRISTOL, CAMBRIDGE, CARDIFF, DURHAM, EDINBURGH, EXETER, GLASGOW, IMPERIAL COLLEGE LONDON, KING'S COLLEGE LONDON, LANCASTER, LEEDS, LIVERPOOL, LONDON SCHOOL OF ECONOMICS, LOUGHBOROUGH, MANCHESTER, NEWCASTLE, NOTTINGHAM, OXFORD, READING, SHEFFIELD, SOUTHAMPTON, ST ANDREWS, STRATHCLYDE, UNIVERSITY COLLEGE LONDON, WARWICK, YORK
Please check with your university careers service for full details of local events.

MINIMUM ENTRY REQUIREMENTS
2.1 Degree

APPLICATION DEADLINE
31st December 2013

FURTHER INFORMATION
www.Top100GraduateEmployers.com
Register now for the latest news, events information and graduate recruitment details for Britain's leading employers.

To save our customers money
every day takes a lot of brain power.
You might say we're single minded about it. Because every single penny saved is a customer delighted. And with 19 million customers, that's big figures. That's why we've been the lowest priced supermarket for the last 15 years. And that's why we need some equally impressive figures to join us. Graduates with a head for business and the attitude to succeed. Outstanding individuals, determined to be our future leaders.
At all costs.
ASDA GRADUATE
PROGRAMME 2014
www.ASDA.jobs/graduates
ASDA
SAVING
YOU MONEY EVERY DAY

ATKINS

www.atkinsglobal.com/careers/graduates

graduates@atkinsglobal.com

twitter.com/atkinsglobal facebook.com/atkinsglobal

youtube.com/user/wsatkinsplc linkedin.com/company/atkins

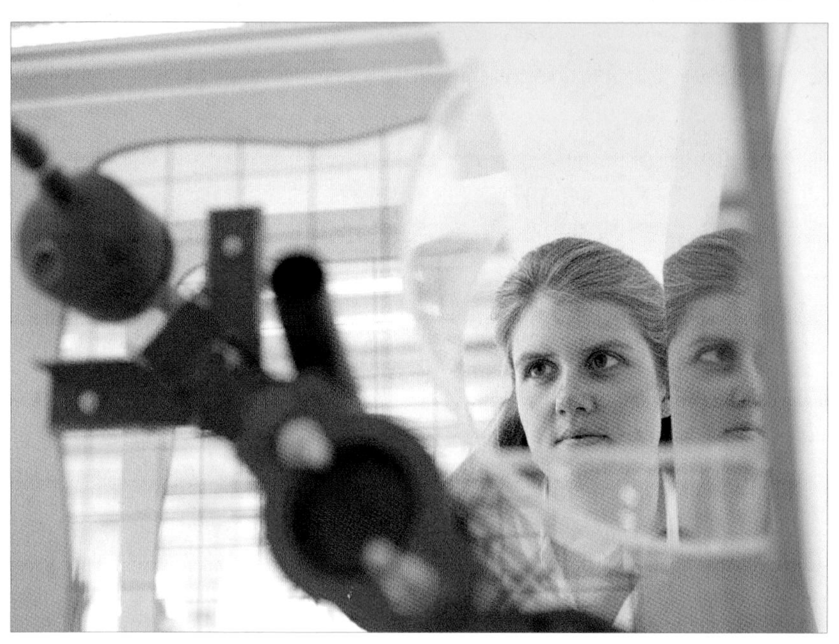

Atkins is one of the world's leading engineering and design consultancies with a reputation for delivering iconic and innovative projects and developing people to be the best. It's a leader in many areas, involved in growth industries such as aerospace, energy, transport and environmental infrastructure.

Atkins has the breadth and depth of experience to respond to the most technically challenging and time-critical infrastructure projects. As the official engineering design services provider for the London 2012 Games, Atkins demonstrated its excellent technical ability to plan, design and enable world class carbon-critical projects.

Atkins is recruiting ambitious graduates who enjoy addressing challenges with creative thinking and quiet brilliance. People who can demonstrate flexibility and drive, who want to explore their own potential and all that a career with Atkins will offer – a world of opportunities.

Atkins provides an environment in which engineers, planners, architects and a myriad of related professionals flourish. Working for the largest UK employer in the engineering and design sector, Atkins' graduates have access to opportunities across a range of locations and business areas. The scope for working on interesting and acclaimed projects with inspiring colleagues is high.

Atkins encourages graduates to drive their own development within a supportive and technically excellent team environment. The company's three year graduate development programme combines project experience with learning modules, graduate forums and events. It also allows each graduate to follow a path that is unique, working towards personal and professional career goals and obtaining relevant Chartership qualifications, under the ongoing guidance of a mentor.

GRADUATE VACANCIES IN 2014

- CONSULTING
- ENGINEERING
- IT
- PROPERTY

NUMBER OF VACANCIES

300+ graduate jobs

LOCATIONS OF VACANCIES

Vacancies also available in Europe, the USA, Asia and elsewhere in the world.

STARTING SALARY FOR 2014

£23,000-£33,000

Plus £2,500 Golden Hello and £2,500 upon completion of Chartership.

UNIVERSITY VISITS IN 2013-14

ABERDEEN, BATH, BIRMINGHAM, BRISTOL, CAMBRIDGE, CARDIFF, GLASGOW, HERIOT-WATT, IMPERIAL COLLEGE LONDON, LEEDS, LOUGHBOROUGH, MANCHESTER, NEWCASTLE, NOTTINGHAM, NOTTINGHAM TRENT, OXFORD, SHEFFIELD, STRATHCLYDE, SURREY, WARWICK

Please check with your university careers service for full details of local events.

MINIMUM ENTRY REQUIREMENTS

2.1 Degree

APPLICATION DEADLINE

Year-round recruitment

Early application advised.

FURTHER INFORMATION

www.Top100GraduateEmployers.com

Register now for the latest news, events information and graduate recruitment details for Britain's leading employers.

www.bakermckenzie.com/londongraduates

londongraduates@bakermckenzie.com 

facebook.com/BakerMcKenzieGraduates 

BAKER & MCKENZIE

Baker & McKenzie is a leading global law firm based in over 70 locations across 46 countries. With a presence in nearly all of the world's leading financial and commercial centres, its strategy is to provide the best combination of local legal and commercial knowledge, international expertise and resources.

London is home to the firm's largest office where Baker & McKenzie has been well established since opening in 1961. With more than 400 legal professionals, the firm has a substantial presence in the legal and business community.

Baker & McKenzie delivers high-quality local solutions across a broad range of practices and global advice in conjunction with our international offices. The firm's client base consists primarily of multinational corporates, based in the UK and elsewhere, and financial institutions. As may be expected of a firm with a very strong international client base, Baker & McKenzie has considerable expertise in acting on, and co-ordinating, cross-border transactions and disputes.

The firm's Corporate and Finance teams regularly advise on, and co-ordinate, complex, cross-border transactions for its clients. As a full service office, Baker & McKenzie covers all the practices expected of a major law firm in the UK, many of which are acclaimed and market-leading.

The firm strives to enable trainees to be the best they can be. It is looking for trainees who are stimulated by intellectual challenge and respect and enjoy the diversity of cultural, social and academic backgrounds found in the Firm. Effective communication skills, together with the ability to be creative and practical problem solvers, team players and to have a sense of humour, are qualities which will help them stand out from the crowd.

GRADUATE VACANCIES IN 2014

LAW

NUMBER OF VACANCIES

34 graduate jobs

For training contracts starting in 2016.

LOCATIONS OF VACANCIES

STARTING SALARY FOR 2014

£39,500

£3,000 joining bonus, £6,000 maintenance grant for GDL and £8,000 maintenance grant for LPC.

UNIVERSITY VISITS IN 2013-14

BELFAST, BIRMINGHAM, BRISTOL, CAMBRIDGE, DURHAM, EDINBURGH, EXETER, KING'S COLLEGE LONDON, LEEDS, LEICESTER, LONDON SCHOOL OF ECONOMICS, MANCHESTER, NOTTINGHAM, OXFORD, SOUTHAMPTON, UNIVERSITY COLLEGE LONDON, WARWICK, YORK

Please check with your university careers service for full details of local events.

MINIMUM ENTRY REQUIREMENTS

2.1 Degree

340 UCAS points

APPLICATION DEADLINE

Law: 31st July 2014

Non-law: 31st July 2014

FURTHER INFORMATION

www.Top100GraduateEmployers.com

Register now for the latest news, events information and graduate recruitment details for Britain's leading employers.

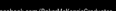

Balfour Beatty

www.balfourbeatty.com/careers

youtube.com/user/BalfourBeattyPlc linkedin.com/company/382657

Balfour Beatty is a global infrastructure group that delivers world class services essential to the development, creation and care of infrastructure assets: from finance and development, through design and project management to construction and maintenance.

Balfour Beatty draws on global knowledge across the infrastructure lifecycle to develop innovative assets to create and support tomorrow's communities, today. Operating in over 80 countries, Balfour Beatty creates and cares for the vital assets that enable societies and economies to grow: road and rail; airports, seaports, tunnels and bridges; health and education facilities; heat, light, power and water; places to live and places to work – the infrastructure that underpins progress. Balfour Beatty has a breadth of capabilities and depth of technical expertise making it a leading global infrastructure business. Without its people, Balfour Beatty couldn't offer four broad capabilities: professional services, construction services, support services and infrastructure investments.

Each year Balfour Beatty recruits around 150 graduates from a mixture of different disciplines. Whilst the majority of graduate jobs are in engineering, environmental, construction management and quantity surveying, Balfour Beatty also welcomes applications from graduates with other degree disciplines. The structure of the graduate programmes may vary by scheme, but each will generally last at least two years.

With experts in every area, graduates learn from the best. Graduates receive excellent training, along with the chance to play a hands-on role in projects from the very start. For ambitious graduates, Balfour Beatty offers more options, responsibility and insight into every part of the infrastructure lifecycle.

Bank of America Merrill Lynch

www.baml.com/campusEMEA

Bank of America is one of the world's largest financial institutions, serving individual consumers, small and middle-market businesses and large corporations. Bank of America Merrill Lynch is a long-established participant in EMEA with a presence since 1922.

With offices in over 30 cities across the region, Bank of America Merrill Lynch offers an integrated and comprehensive set of products and services across Global Corporate & Investment Banking, Global Markets, Wealth Management and Consumer Card, serving the needs of individual, corporate, institutional and government clients, combining the best of local knowledge and global expertise to offer bespoke solutions no matter their location.

Full-time and internship programmes are available in the following areas: Capital Markets, Compliance, Corporate Banking, Global Loan Products, Global Markets, Global Transaction Services, Investment Banking, Human Resources, Quantitative Management, Research, Risk and Technology. Graduates will gain a breadth of knowledge and experience and be positioned for great career opportunities.

Bank of America Merrill Lynch encourages a diverse, inclusive workplace. This gives the business the advantage of understanding and meeting the needs of diverse clients and shareholders, and provides fresh ideas and perspectives, which promote ingenuity. By joining Bank of America Merrill Lynch, graduates will receive the highest level of training and mentoring support. Furthermore, their commitment to improving the quality of life within the local community and taking care of the environment means they can get involved in a number of volunteering initiatives.

GRADUATE VACANCIES IN 2014

- FINANCE
- HUMAN RESOURCES
- INVESTMENT BANKING
- IT

NUMBER OF VACANCIES

200+ graduate jobs

LOCATIONS OF VACANCIES

Vacancies also available in Europe and elsewhere in the world.

STARTING SALARY FOR 2014

£Competitive

UNIVERSITY VISITS IN 2013-14

BRISTOL, CAMBRIDGE, DURHAM, EDINBURGH, IMPERIAL COLLEGE LONDON, KING'S COLLEGE LONDON, LONDON SCHOOL OF ECONOMICS, LOUGHBOROUGH, MANCHESTER, NOTTINGHAM, OXFORD, QUEEN MARY LONDON, SOUTHAMPTON, ST ANDREWS, UNIVERSITY COLLEGE LONDON, WARWICK

Please check with your university careers service for full details of local events.

MINIMUM ENTRY REQUIREMENTS

2.1 Degree

Relevant degree required for some roles.

APPLICATION DEADLINE

Please see website for full details.

FURTHER INFORMATION

www.Top100GraduateEmployers.com

Register now for the latest news, events information and graduate recruitment details for Britain's leading employers.

BARCLAYS

barclays.com/joinus

Today, you will
raise expectations
higher.

140,000 people. Over 50 countries. A long tradition of innovation that remains at the heart of the business today. These are just a few of the things that make Barclays a major global financial services provider. But what truly sets the bank apart are its future ambitions and the actions it's taking to achieve them.

Barclays is shaping the future of its business. Driven by strong values and a clear direction, it is focusing on one core purpose: helping people achieve their ambitions – in the right way. This includes its graduates and interns. Barclays offers a remarkable breadth of opportunities for students, undergraduates, graduates and postgraduates right across its business.

There are openings in Corporate and Investment Banking, Retail and Business Banking and Wealth and Investment Management, as well as a host of crucial business support functions such as Technology, HR and Marketing. Applications are welcome from graduates from all disciplines.

Every programme presents distinct challenges and opportunities. But whichever part of Barclays graduates join, they can expect immediate responsibility and continued support. Their development will be tailored to their needs, from the intensive initial training through to ongoing professional education and far beyond the programme. And they will be empowered to think innovatively and seize opportunities to inspire progress.

Graduates are playing their part in change right across Barclays. So as well as a strong academic record and a commercial outlook, new graduates coming into Barclays need to be ready to help drive the business forward. As they do, they'll take their own careers forward too.

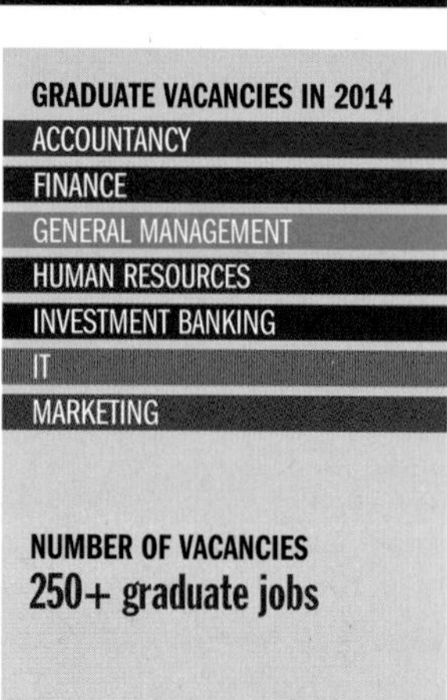

GRADUATE VACANCIES IN 2014
- ACCOUNTANCY
- FINANCE
- GENERAL MANAGEMENT
- HUMAN RESOURCES
- INVESTMENT BANKING
- IT
- MARKETING

NUMBER OF VACANCIES
250+ graduate jobs

LOCATIONS OF VACANCIES

Vacancies also available in Europe, Asia, the USA and elsewhere in the world.

STARTING SALARY FOR 2014
£Competitive

UNIVERSITY VISITS IN 2013-14
BATH, BRISTOL, CAMBRIDGE, DURHAM, EDINBURGH, GLASGOW, IMPERIAL COLLEGE LONDON, LONDON SCHOOL OF ECONOMICS, LOUGHBOROUGH, MANCHESTER, NOTTINGHAM, OXFORD, ST ANDREWS, STRATHCLYDE, UNIVERSITY COLLEGE LONDON, WARWICK
Please check with your university careers service for full details of local events.

APPLICATION DEADLINE
15th November 2013

FURTHER INFORMATION
www.Top100GraduateEmployers.com
Register now for the latest news, events information and graduate recruitment details for Britain's leading employers.

BBC

www.bbc.co.uk/careers

twitter.com/BBCTrainees & BBCRecruitment

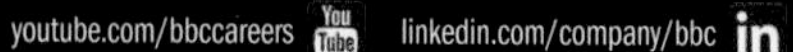

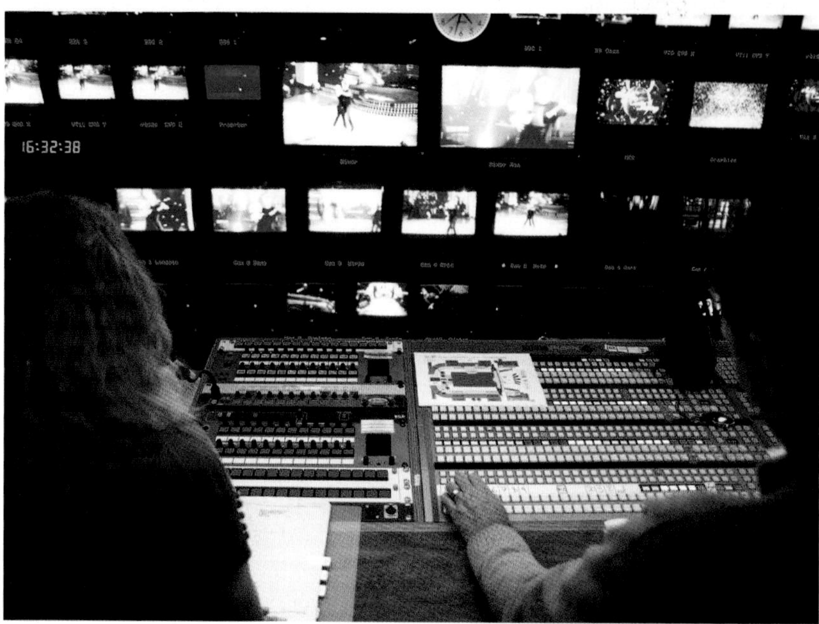

The BBC is one of the world's best-known broadcasting brands. Roughly 97% of UK adults use its services each week – not to mention millions more around the globe. It's a diverse and fast-moving environment, and as well as graduates to join the corporation's renowned Journalism, Design and Production trainee schemes, the BBC also looks for talent in other areas.

Allowing viewers, listeners and readers to consume media in a constantly evolving digital, on-demand and online world, BBC Future Media designs, develops and runs digital services and products that have shaped the entire broadcasting industry. Their pioneering work on HD and the BBC iPlayer, and recently the first truly digital Olympic Games and Glastonbury festival, has had a global impact, and graduates here are key to getting content to audiences anytime, anywhere and anyhow. More than that, they're key to the future of broadcasting.

The BBC never stands still – and neither do its graduates. Digital Media Graduates are supported from aspiring developer to industry expert, and BBC Technology Trainees earn a Masters in Digital Broadcast Technology as they help deliver great content to global audiences. HR Graduates, meanwhile, build on their professional skills with exciting change and people projects. There are a range of schemes on offer and the BBC looks for graduates with degrees relevant to these areas, particularly when it comes to technology-based programmes.

Together, BBC graduates will transform the way media is consumed and create brand new broadcasting experiences. They'll also receive some of the best training in the industry and, as many BBC managers and programme makers began their careers as trainees, talented graduates could have an exceptional future ahead of them.

GRADUATE VACANCIES IN 2014

- ENGINEERING
- HUMAN RESOURCES
- IT
- MEDIA
- RESEARCH & DEVELOPMENT

NUMBER OF VACANCIES

200 graduate jobs

LOCATIONS OF VACANCIES

STARTING SALARY FOR 2014

£20,000-£25,000

UNIVERSITY VISITS IN 2013-14

Please check with your university careers service for full details of local events.

MINIMUM ENTRY REQUIREMENTS

2.1 Degree

Relevant degree required for some roles.

APPLICATION DEADLINE

Year-round recruitment

FURTHER INFORMATION

www.Top100GraduateEmployers.com

Register now for the latest news, events information and graduate recruitment details for Britain's leading employers.

BlackRock®

www.blackrockoncampus.com

facebook.com/BlackRock  EMEACampusRecruitment@blackrock.com

youtube.com/blackrock  twitter.com/BlackRockCampus

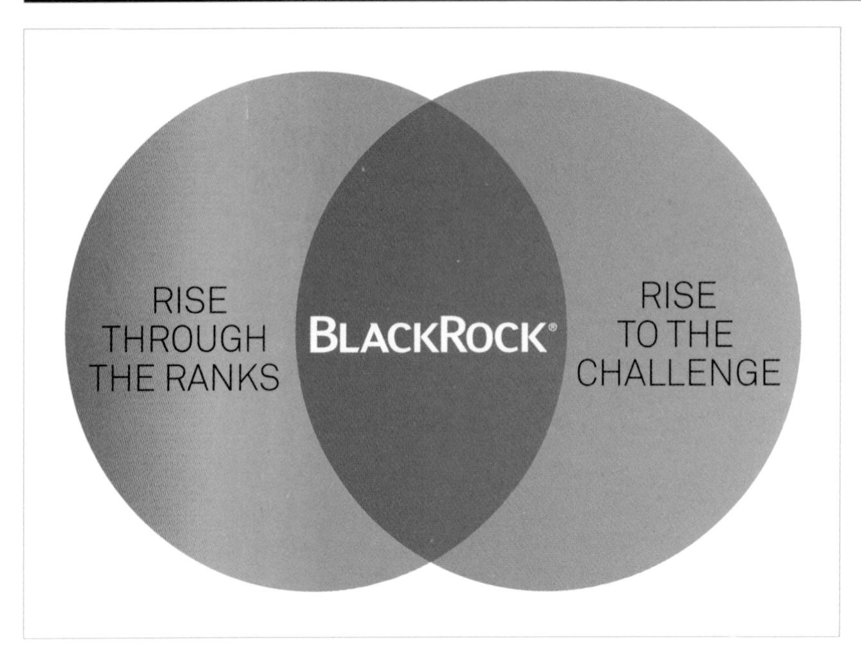

As the world's largest asset manager, BlackRock brings together financial leadership, worldwide reach and state-of-the-art technology to provide answers to the millions of investors from across the globe who entrust their financial futures to the company.

At BlackRock a collaborative culture unites all the business groups – as does a common focus on helping the firm's clients and the communities in which BlackRock employees work and live. BlackRock seeks the best and brightest talent to join a dynamic and diverse environment that inspires high performance.

The Graduate Programme at BlackRock is an ideal opportunity for natural-born problem solvers, innovators and future leaders to work for a firm that has been called in by some of the world's largest companies and governments to find solutions for their most pressing financial challenges.

BlackRock is committed to harnessing every graduate's potential, developing their expertise and advancing their career. All members of the Graduate Programme begin their BlackRock career with a two-week orientation in New York. Following this, graduates benefit from a structured curriculum of ongoing training throughout the first year and beyond, all designed to maximise their business knowledge and individual effectiveness.

Over the last 25 years BlackRock has built up a network of more than 60 offices worldwide including London, Edinburgh, New York, San Francisco and Hong Kong, which gives graduates ample room to move across businesses and borders. As a global firm, the work is diverse and the opportunities are limitless, with positions in Advisory & Client Support, Analytics & Risk, Client Businesses, Corporate Operations, Investment and Technology.

GRADUATE VACANCIES IN 2014

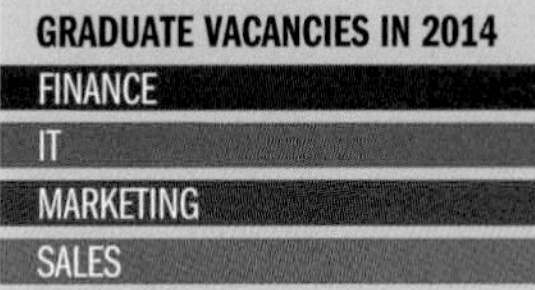

NUMBER OF VACANCIES
90 graduate jobs

LOCATIONS OF VACANCIES

Vacancies also available in Europe.

STARTING SALARY FOR 2014
£Competitive

UNIVERSITY VISITS IN 2013-14
BATH, BELFAST, BRISTOL, CAMBRIDGE, DURHAM, EDINBURGH, HERIOT-WATT, IMPERIAL COLLEGE LONDON, KING'S COLLEGE LONDON, LONDON SCHOOL OF ECONOMICS, MANCHESTER, NOTTINGHAM, OXFORD, ST ANDREWS, STRATHCLYDE, TRINITY COLLEGE DUBLIN, UNIVERSITY COLLEGE DUBLIN, UNIVERSITY COLLEGE LONDON, WARWICK
Please check with your university careers service for full details of local events.

MINIMUM ENTRY REQUIREMENTS
2.1 Degree

APPLICATION DEADLINE
17th November 2013

FURTHER INFORMATION
www.Top100GraduateEmployers.com
Register now for the latest news, events information and graduate recruitment details for Britain's leading employers.

www.boots.jobs/talentprogrammes

youtube.com/user/bootsrecruitment linkedin.com/company/boots

Boots Talent Programmes 2013

Tomorrow's Future Leaders in #Finance #IT #Marketing #Retailing Apply now

Like Comment Share

As the UK's leading pharmacy-led health and beauty retailer and one of the country's most trusted household names, Boots is evolving in the changing world of retail and the future looks very bright. To help the company succeed, Boots needs a strong team of people who genuinely love driving business performance by creating "feel good" moments for customers.

On the Boots Graduate Programme, there are four exciting, involving and evolving areas of the business to choose from.

The Retail Management Programme develops graduates as store leaders capable of offering Boots customers the legendary experience they expect each time they walk into a store.

On the Brand, Buying and Marketing Programme, successful candidates will explore how to develop, source and market Boots' renowned brands, including No7 and Botanics, as well as a huge range of external brands.

The Finance Programme offers graduates more than just experience in financial accounting, management information and business partnering. They'll be part of the department that is creating the business framework for now and the future. Boots will also fund a relevant financial qualification, and give them the opportunity to work in an international role.

As part of the Technology Leadership Programme, graduates will be driving IT solutions to meet the demands of this fast growing business now and in the future.

While a relevant business, retail or financial degree is ideal, what's really important is a passion for retail and a real desire to drive the company successfully into the future. Develop an amazing career with Boots and realise why the organisation is good for graduates.

PURCHASING

RETAILING

NUMBER OF VACANCIES
50 graduate jobs

LOCATIONS OF VACANCIES

STARTING SALARY FOR 2014
£Competitive

UNIVERSITY VISITS IN 2013-14
Please check with your university careers service for full details of local events.

MINIMUM ENTRY REQUIREMENTS
Relevant degree required for some roles.

APPLICATION DEADLINE
30th November 2013

FURTHER INFORMATION
www.Top100GraduateEmployers.com
Register now for the latest news, events information and graduate recruitment details for Britain's leading employers.

BCG

THE BOSTON CONSULTING GROUP

www.bcglondon.com

lonrecruiting@bcg.com

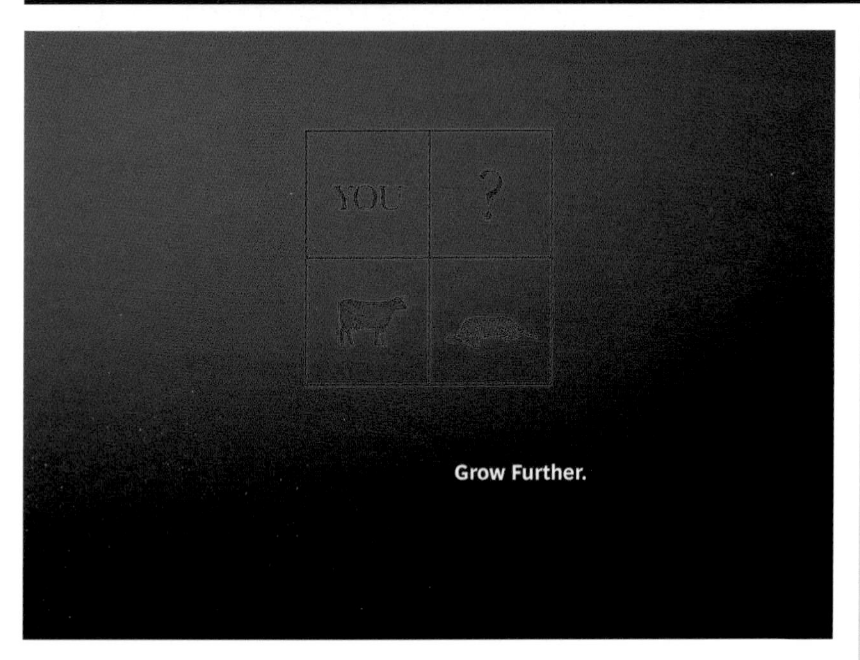

GRADUATE VACANCIES IN 2014

CONSULTING

NUMBER OF VACANCIES
No fixed quota

LOCATIONS OF VACANCIES

Vacancies also available elsewhere in the world.

STARTING SALARY FOR 2014
£Competitive

UNIVERSITY VISITS IN 2013-14
CAMBRIDGE, IMPERIAL COLLEGE LONDON, LONDON SCHOOL OF ECONOMICS, OXFORD
Please check with your university careers service for full details of local events.

MINIMUM ENTRY REQUIREMENTS
2.1 Degree

APPLICATION DEADLINE
3rd November 2013

FURTHER INFORMATION
www.Top100GraduateEmployers.com
Register now for the latest news, events information and graduate recruitment details for Britain's leading employers.

The Boston Consulting Group is a global management consulting firm and the world's leading advisor on business strategy. BCG partners with clients from all sectors and regions to navigate demanding business environments, identify their highest-value opportunities and transform their businesses.

BCG's customised, collaborative approach combines deep insight into the dynamics of companies and markets with close collaboration at all levels of the client organisation. This ensures that its clients achieve sustainable competitive advantage, build more capable organisations and secure lasting results. Since 1990, the firm has grown at an industry-beating 15 percent annually. BCG is looking for people (new graduates or young professionals) to further strengthen its teams – people as passionate as BCG is about creating lasting change.

As part of a winning team, BCG consultants work daily with the world's leading companies to solve their toughest issues and transform their businesses. BCG consultants collaborate in close-knit teams in a true partnership environment. They are inspired, challenged and mentored by the best business minds and grow by gaining unique client experience and exposure, driving client results, and helping leaders in business not just play better, but change the rules of the game.

BCG offers an unmatched platform for personal growth. Its targeted international training programme supports the development of a comprehensive toolkit of business, management and interpersonal skills. In addition, BCG sponsors its consultants in MBA studies at leading business schools, supports (social impact) secondments with world-class clients, and provides work opportunities in any of its 78 offices around the world. The knowledge, experience and skills gained will provide the springboard to excel in any field within BCG or beyond.

bp

bp.com/ukgraduates

facebook.com/bpcareers 

I DISCOVERED TO BE
AN EXPERT
MEANS ALWAYS BEING A STUDENT
UNI HONG, ORIGINATOR, SINGAPORE

Heat. Light. Power. Mobility. Materials for the products that define modern life. All are made possible by oil and gas. Delivering them safely, sustainably and cost effectively is what BP's business is all about. And remains one of the biggest challenges in the world today.

BP offers graduate opportunities in engineering, science, business and trading. Successful applicants will find out what it takes to deliver energy safely to the world and discover how BP and its people find, develop and produce essential sources of energy and how that energy is turned into products everyone on the planet depends on every day.

Graduates who join BP will find out how BP's people make some truly amazing discoveries to meet that challenge. Both in terms of scientific and engineering breakthroughs and what BP as a team are capable of.

BP recruits ambitious graduates at every stage of the energy life cycle – from geoscientists sending shock waves through the earth to find new oil and gas reserves and engineers building platforms in the ocean to extract them, to traders anticipating and reacting to changes in the markets around them.

Designed for future business leaders, world-class scientists or ground-breaking engineers, BP's graduate programmes are designed to help students develop the skills and experience they need. And at the same time, they get a unique insight into BP's work and discover how incredible an organisation it is to be part of.

Because BP offers such a breadth of opportunity in engineering, science, business and trading, students could come to BP with a good degree in practically any discipline. Every bit as important will be the individual attributes and personal qualities students bring.

GRADUATE VACANCIES IN 2014

- ACCOUNTANCY
- ENGINEERING
- FINANCE
- GENERAL MANAGEMENT
- HUMAN RESOURCES
- INVESTMENT BANKING
- IT
- LOGISTICS
- PURCHASING
- RESEARCH & DEVELOPMENT
- RETAILING
- SALES

NUMBER OF VACANCIES
220 graduate jobs

LOCATIONS OF VACANCIES

STARTING SALARY FOR 2014
£33,000
Plus £3,000 settling-in allowance.

UNIVERSITY VISITS IN 2013-14
BATH, BIRMINGHAM, CAMBRIDGE, DURHAM, IMPERIAL COLLEGE LONDON, MANCHESTER, NOTTINGHAM, OXFORD, STRATHCLYDE
Please check with your university careers service for full details of local events.

MINIMUM ENTRY REQUIREMENTS
2.1 Degree

APPLICATION DEADLINE
Varies by function
See website for full details.

FURTHER INFORMATION
www.Top100GraduateEmployers.com
Register now for the latest news, events information and graduate recruitment details for Britain's leading employers.

BA flies 37 million customers and 788,000 tonnes of cargo to 177 destinations across the globe every year. Its reputation for customer service and quality is a credit to its 40,000 colleagues across 75 countries. Together, they are responsible for an annual revenue of over £10 billion.

If the past decade has brought both challenge and opportunity, it's the future which genuinely excites. BA is on a journey, a journey its people live, feel and shape each day. And the journey they're on is to be experienced – because few organisations inspire such belonging, purpose and genuine belief.

BA is a business with breadth and complexity and at its heart are its people. Graduates joining BA will be a key part of this journey that's about a greater purpose; the promise BA makes to each of its customers every day: To Fly. To Serve.

The talented graduates who join BA work on real jobs with real responsibilities. This takes ambition, resilience, collaboration and the drive to go above and beyond. In return they can expect to work across different business areas, to be involved in key business decisions and have opportunities to travel and to work in different locations. In fact, with attractive colleague travel benefits BA's graduates all have the opportunity to see the world and share unique experiences.

There are opportunities to become one of their Commercial Analysts or Leaders for Business as well as in IT, HR, Procurement, Finance, Operational Research, Engineering and World Cargo. Whichever career path is taken, each will start with a comprehensive induction. Then each programme has its own structured development plan to make sure graduates have all the support and opportunities they need to excel and live the journey.

GRADUATE VACANCIES IN 2014

- CONSULTING
- ENGINEERING
- FINANCE
- GENERAL MANAGEMENT
- HUMAN RESOURCES
- IT
- LOGISTICS
- PURCHASING
- RESEARCH & DEVELOPMENT

NUMBER OF VACANCIES
Up to 70 graduate jobs

LOCATIONS OF VACANCIES

STARTING SALARY FOR 2014
£24,500-£28,000

UNIVERSITY VISITS IN 2013-14
BATH, BIRMINGHAM, BRISTOL, BRUNEL, CAMBRIDGE, LONDON SCHOOL OF ECONOMICS, LOUGHBOROUGH, NEWCASTLE, NOTTINGHAM, SHEFFIELD, ST ANDREWS, UNIVERSITY COLLEGE LONDON, WARWICK
Please check with your university careers service for full details of local events.

MINIMUM ENTRY REQUIREMENTS
2.1 Degree

APPLICATION DEADLINE
Please see website for full details.

FURTHER INFORMATION
www.Top100GraduateEmployers.com
Register now for the latest news, events information and graduate recruitment details for Britain's leading employers.

BRITISH AIRWAYS

TO BELONG
TO BE CONNECTED

BT

www.btgraduates.com

twitter.com/btgradcareers facebook.com/BTGraduateCareers

Welcome to a world of innovation. BT are one of the world's leading providers of innovative IT and communication services. They're always looking for new ways to help businesses and people become more connected, more productive and more competitive.

But staying ahead in the industry isn't just about technology. It's about people too. People who want to challenge the norm, think of new and better ways to do things and work as part of a team to make them happen. Diversity is at the very heart of the company. In order to provide the very best products and services to their varied customer base they need a diverse workforce to imagine, create and deliver the solutions required both now and into the future. This means creating a working environment that includes and recognises such diversity.

So what makes a successful BT graduate? Leadership potential? Teamworking ability? Creativity? Enthusiasm? Or communication skills? BT looks for all of these qualities. And more. They look for people who don't wait to be told what to do, and who can't wait to get involved.

BT graduates work on real projects, with real responsibility from the start. Whatever they're involved in – whether it's technology, business management, marketing, sales, HR, or legal – they're encouraged to take the initiative.

It's about taking talent and developing future leaders. Throughout the programme, graduates benefit from ongoing training, both on the job and in the classroom. From talent master classes, through to leadership development and commercial awareness as well as professional development, every opportunity is there to be seized. There's huge scope for graduates to shape their own career. To make the most of their leadership potential. And to get connected to the big wide world of BT.

GRADUATE VACANCIES IN 2014

- CONSULTING
- ENGINEERING
- GENERAL MANAGEMENT
- HUMAN RESOURCES
- IT
- LAW
- MARKETING
- RESEARCH & DEVELOPMENT
- SALES

NUMBER OF VACANCIES

Around 200 graduate jobs

LOCATIONS OF VACANCIES

STARTING SALARY FOR 2014

£27,750-£31,500

UNIVERSITY VISITS IN 2013-14

ASTON, BATH, BELFAST, BIRMINGHAM, BRISTOL, CAMBRIDGE, CITY, DURHAM, EDINBURGH, ESSEX, GLASGOW, IMPERIAL COLLEGE LONDON, LANCASTER, LEEDS, MANCHESTER, NOTTINGHAM, OXFORD, SHEFFIELD, SOUTHAMPTON, STRATHCLYDE, WARWICK, YORK

Please check with your university careers service for full details of local events.

MINIMUM ENTRY REQUIREMENTS

2.1 Degree

320 UCAS points

280 points for Technology.
Relevant degree required for some roles.

APPLICATION DEADLINE

Varies by function

FURTHER INFORMATION

www.Top100GraduateEmployers.com

Register now for the latest news, events information and graduate recruitment details for Britain's leading employers.

cruk.org/graduates

recruitment@cancer.org.uk

IT'LL TAKE BRAVE, SMART MINDED PEOPLE TO HELP US BEAT CANCER SOONER.
PEOPLE LIKE YOU.

Cancer. Be afraid. Cancer Research UK is a world-leading organisation and a prestigious funder of science. Day after day, it works to find new and better ways to prevent, detect and treat cancer. Its vision is to bring forward the day when all cancers are cured.

Every step the charity makes towards beating cancer sooner relies on every person, every team and every effort. Now they are looking for brave, smart minded individuals to continue to achieve their goals. Its graduates are passionate in their work, relentlessly determined, unafraid to challenge, stand-out communicators and effective relationship-builders. Not to mention, ready and willing to make a real contribution to bring Cancer Research UK closer to its bold ambition.

What does a graduate scheme at an organisation like this offer? All graduates are put through their paces from the very beginning. Whether joining Cancer Research UK's Fundraising & Marketing; Science; Policy, Information & Communications; IT or Corporate streams, they will have the exciting opportunity to switch roles every six months and experience four diverse business areas over the course of two years.

Graduates receive support and challenge from senior mentors, peers and placement managers along their journey. They also benefit from a combination of on-the-job learning and formal training whilst transitioning between placements. Graduates are expected to gain a permanent job at the end of the scheme, subject to performance and business need.

As well as graduate opportunities, Cancer Research UK offers a vast array of volunteering opportunities including award-winning twelve-week internships.

Join Cancer Research UK and help beat cancer sooner.

GRADUATE VACANCIES IN 2014

- FINANCE
- GENERAL MANAGEMENT
- HUMAN RESOURCES
- IT
- MARKETING
- RESEARCH & DEVELOPMENT
- RETAILING

NUMBER OF VACANCIES
6 graduate jobs

LOCATIONS OF VACANCIES

STARTING SALARY FOR 2014
£24,000

UNIVERSITY VISITS IN 2013-14
CAMBRIDGE, EXETER, IMPERIAL COLLEGE LONDON, KING'S COLLEGE LONDON, LEEDS, OXFORD, READING, SOUTHAMPTON, ST ANDREWS, UNIVERSITY COLLEGE LONDON, WARWICK, YORK
Please check with your university careers service for full details of local events.

MINIMUM ENTRY REQUIREMENTS
2.1 Degree

APPLICATION DEADLINE
January 2014

FURTHER INFORMATION
www.Top100GraduateEmployers.com
Register now for the latest news, events information and graduate recruitment details for Britain's leading employers.

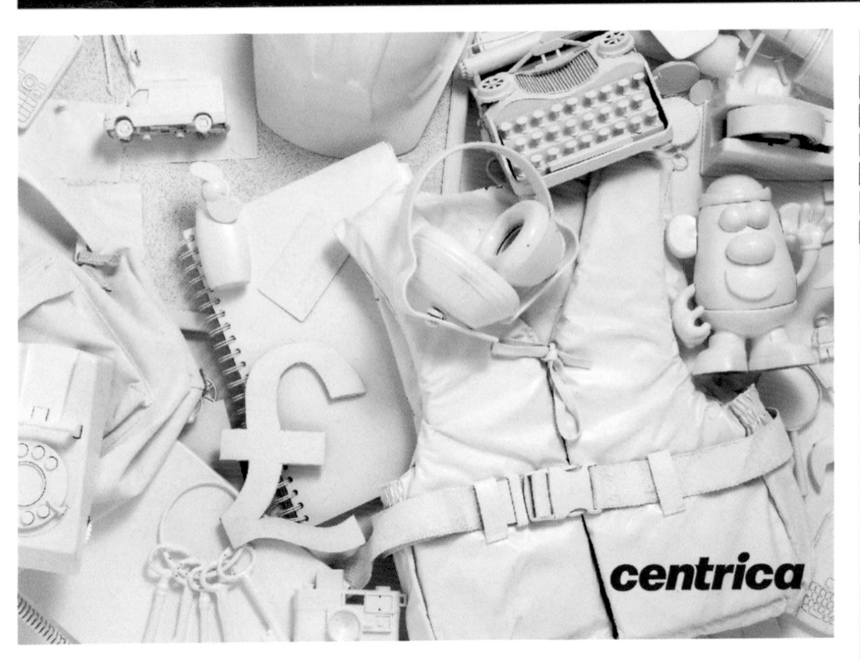

Centrica is an international energy company that sources, generates, processes, stores, trades, supplies, services and helps its customers save energy. Securing energy to power the future is an important priority for Centrica, and the company is making vital investments across the entire energy spectrum.

As a top 30 FTSE 100 company with over 25 million customer accounts, a £22 billion turnover and more than 34,000 employees, Centrica is the parent company for a range of global brands. British Gas and Direct Energy supply power and related services in the UK and North America respectively; Direct Energy and Centrica Energy in the UK manage power generation, gas and oil production and trading operations to ensure day-to-day demand is met, and Centrica Storage is the largest gas storage facility in the UK.

Graduates could be getting involved in any area of the energy lifecycle – from exploration and production with Centrica Energy, to front-line customer service management at British Gas – although the exact role will depend on which of the schemes they join. The graduate programme has been designed to offer a broad grounding in the business; those who are ambitious and commercially savvy have an outstanding opportunity to be a future business leader in this diverse organisation.

Developing graduates is important to Centrica; graduate talent boards ensure they have the opportunity to fulfil their potential and are equipped with the right skills and behaviours to help grow the business and implement Centrica's strategy. It all adds up to an award-winning programme that offers graduates who are up for big challenges the opportunity to get involved in a variety of areas – as well as receiving support and reward along the way.

GRADUATE VACANCIES IN 2014

ENGINEERING
FINANCE
GENERAL MANAGEMENT
HUMAN RESOURCES
IT
MARKETING

NUMBER OF VACANCIES
60+ graduate jobs

LOCATIONS OF VACANCIES

STARTING SALARY FOR 2014
£Competitive

UNIVERSITY VISITS IN 2013-14
CAMBRIDGE, DURHAM, IMPERIAL COLLEGE LONDON, LANCASTER, LOUGHBOROUGH, MANCHESTER, NOTTINGHAM, OXFORD, SHEFFIELD, SOUTHAMPTON, STRATHCLYDE, WARWICK
Please check with your university careers service for full details of local events.

MINIMUM ENTRY REQUIREMENTS
Relevant degree required for some roles.

APPLICATION DEADLINE
Please see website for full details.

FURTHER INFORMATION
www.Top100GraduateEmployers.com
Register now for the latest news, events information and graduate recruitment details for Britain's leading employers.

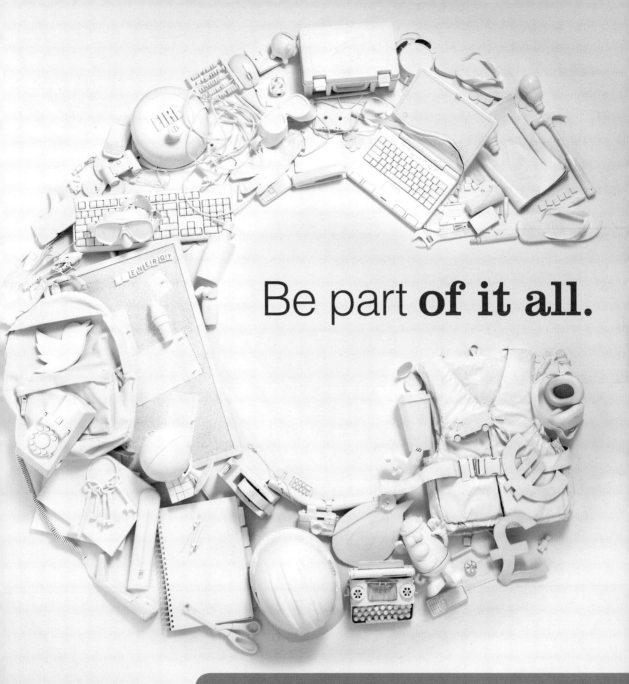

www.4Talent.com

facebook.com/C4PeopleDevelopment · peopledevelopment@channel4.co.uk

youtube.com/user/c4people · twitter.com/4Talent

Channel 4 is a unique organisation: a public service broadcaster with a distinctive creative remit, funded within the marketplace, existing to provide a range of distinctive, challenging and provocative content. Their portfolio includes Channel 4, E4, More4, Film4, 4Music and 4Seven.

As a publisher-broadcaster, Channel 4 is required to commission UK content from the independent production sector. They are a major investor in the UK's creative economy, working with around 400 creative companies every year and investing significantly in training and talent development throughout the industry.

Channel 4 offers a range of work-related programmes for graduates, such as the Graduate, Scholarship and Production Trainee Programmes. The Graduate Programme is open to people who have finished university and are ready to enter the world of work. Successful candidates will gain hands on experience and gain an MA in creative leadership. The Scholarship Programme is not for the faint hearted. While working at Channel 4, graduates are given the opportunity to study and gain a PhD. The Production Trainee Programme is perfect for those who want a career in production. This programme is open to anyone of any age from any background. All Channel 4 asks for is a passion for TV.

Channel 4 prides itself on the wide range of passionate and talented people that they employ. They believe that a diverse workforce promotes creativity, which for them is the life blood of what they do. Channel 4's ethos is that creative thinking, both on and off screen, is significantly better by embracing diversity in its widest sense. By attracting people from all backgrounds and walks of life, they have created an environment in which everyone feels free to be who they are at work.

GRADUATE VACANCIES IN 2014
- MARKETING
- MEDIA
- RESEARCH & DEVELOPMENT
- SALES

NUMBER OF VACANCIES
2-4 graduate jobs

LOCATIONS OF VACANCIES

STARTING SALARY FOR 2014
£24,000
Plus a performance-related bonus.

UNIVERSITY VISITS IN 2013-14
BELFAST, GLASGOW, MANCHESTER, SHEFFIELD, UNIVERSITY COLLEGE LONDON
Please check with your university careers service for full details of local events.

MINIMUM ENTRY REQUIREMENTS
2.1 Degree

APPLICATION DEADLINE
Varies by function

FURTHER INFORMATION
www.Top100GraduateEmployers.com
Register now for the latest news, events information and graduate recruitment details for Britain's leading employers.

www.oncampus.citi.com

campus.queries@citi.com

twitter.com/citigradsEMEA facebook.com/citigradsEMEA 

Since Citi opened its first office in New York in 1812, it has answered the needs of economies, businesses and communities in hundreds of cities, in over 160 countries, thriving in the most challenging times over a 200 year history. Citi's global presence isn't just a question of size, it's a way of thinking.

A career with Citi means being part of a global firm that provides the most forward-thinking financial products and solutions to the most enterprising corporations, institutions, governments and individuals around the world.

Citi's success is driven by its exceptional people – their passion, dedication and entrepreneurship – and it will be graduates who will shape its future. At Citi, learning doesn't stop at graduation and there are many ways to embark on a rewarding career path, enjoying the global opportunities and long-term training and development initiatives experienced by over 260,000 employees worldwide.

Citi offers full-time and internship opportunities across a number of its business areas, including Investment Banking, Corporate Banking, Capital Markets Origination, Sales & Trading, Citi Transaction Services, Private Bank, Risk Management, Human Resources and Operations & Technology. Citi also offers insight programmes enabling students in their first year (or in their second year of a four year course) to experience firsthand the Citi culture and environment. Graduates interested in this industry with drive, commitment and a passion for learning are encouraged to apply.

This is the opportunity to be part of an exciting period in the development of the global financial services industry, working with the brightest minds to drive responsible, positive change across the organisation, the banking industry, and beyond.

GRADUATE VACANCIES IN 2014

FINANCE

HUMAN RESOURCES

INVESTMENT BANKING

IT

NUMBER OF VACANCIES

200 graduate jobs

LOCATIONS OF VACANCIES

Vacancies also available in Europe and elsewhere in the world.

STARTING SALARY FOR 2014

£Competitive

Relocation allowance, private healthcare, life assurance and pension scheme (company contribution).

UNIVERSITY VISITS IN 2013-14

BATH, BELFAST, BRISTOL, CAMBRIDGE, CITY, DURHAM, EDINBURGH, EXETER, IMPERIAL COLLEGE LONDON, KING'S COLLEGE LONDON, LONDON SCHOOL OF ECONOMICS, MANCHESTER, NOTTINGHAM, OXFORD, ST ANDREWS, TRINITY COLLEGE DUBLIN, UNIVERSITY COLLEGE LONDON, WARWICK

Please check with your university careers service for full details of local events.

MINIMUM ENTRY REQUIREMENTS

2.1 Degree

320 UCAS points

APPLICATION DEADLINE

Early application advised.
Please see website for full details.

FURTHER INFORMATION

www.Top100GraduateEmployers.com

Register now for the latest news, events information and graduate recruitment details for Britain's leading employers.

FASTSTREAM

facebook.com/faststream | faststream@parity.net

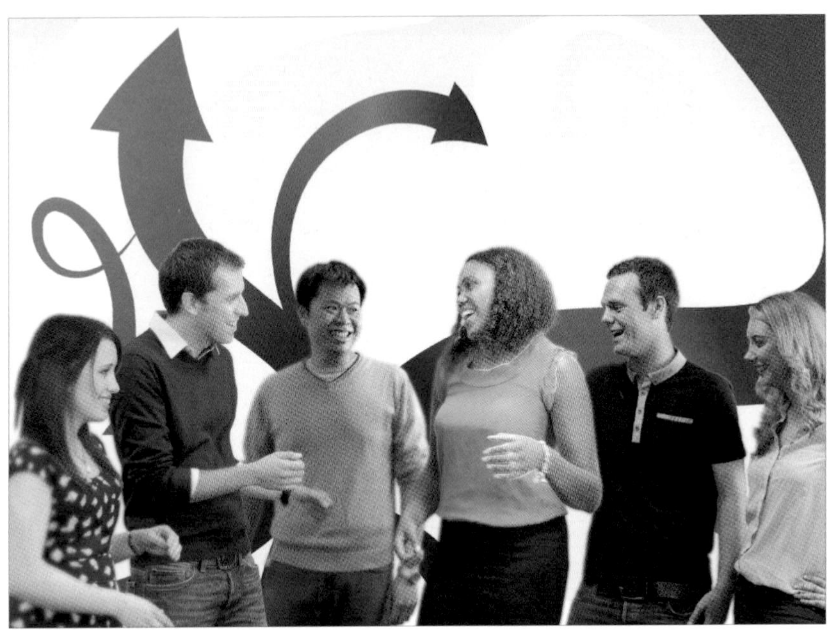

Education. Health. Justice. Employment. Defence. Transport. Climate change. International development. Foreign affairs. If the government has a policy on something, it is guaranteed that Fast Streamers are working at the heart of it, putting their brains and their skills at the disposal of the whole of society.

The Fast Stream is an accelerated learning and development programme for graduates with the motivation and the potential to become the future leaders of the Civil Service. Fast Streamers are given considerable responsibility from the outset: they are stretched and challenged on a daily basis, and they move regularly between posts to gain a wide range of contrasting experiences and build up an impressive portfolio of skills and knowledge.

Work ranges across professional areas including operational delivery, policy development, corporate services, people management, commercial awareness, financial management and project management, giving Fast Streamers a wide understanding of how government delivers public services. Comprehensive training and development combined with on-the-job learning and support is provided. Successful applicants will receive an excellent package of benefits.

There's no such thing as a typical Fast Streamer, and graduates from widely diverse backgrounds are attracted to it. The only thing common to them all is that they are excited by the idea of making a positive and highly visible impact on different walks of life. Society is best served by a Civil Service which is as diverse as itself.

There are opportunities available across the UK in all areas of government, offering graduates a unique perspective of work at the heart of current affairs and key government agendas. There's no limit to where they could lead on the Civil Service Fast Stream. All degree disciplines are welcome.

GRADUATE VACANCIES IN 2014

- ENGINEERING
- GENERAL MANAGEMENT
- HUMAN RESOURCES
- IT

NUMBER OF VACANCIES
800+ graduate jobs

LOCATIONS OF VACANCIES

STARTING SALARY FOR 2014
£25,000-£27,000

UNIVERSITY VISITS IN 2013-14
Please check with your university careers service for full details of local events.

MINIMUM ENTRY REQUIREMENTS
2.2 Degree

APPLICATION DEADLINE
30th October 2013
The Analytical Fast Stream reopens in February 2014 and closes in April. See website for further details.

FURTHER INFORMATION
www.Top100GraduateEmployers.com
Register now for the latest news, events information and graduate recruitment details for Britain's leading employers.

C L I F F O R D
C H A N C E

www.cliffordchance.com/gradsuk

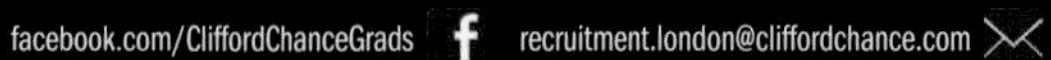

youtube.com/user/CliffordChanceGrads  twitter.com/CCGradsUK 

Every year Clifford Chance looks for individuals who share the firm's ambition to remain right at the forefront of international law firms. Graduates who join Clifford Chance will become part of a team dedicated to tackling some of the most complex and fascinating legal issues facing the world today.

Clifford Chance works both internationally and domestically with a full range of clients, from multi-national and domestic corporates to financial institutions, regulatory authorities, supranational bodies, governments and government agencies. This is a firm where day-to-day work is often 'game-changing', and where trainees work on transformational deals and issues.

Clifford Chance is regularly singled out for the quality of its client service and legal expertise. Recent accolades include: International Law Firm of the Year 2013 (Chambers Global), Middle East Law Firm of the Year 2013 (Chambers Global), European Law Firm of the Year 2013 (Chambers Europe), International Law Firm of the Year 2013 (IFLR Asia Awards), Financial Regulation Team of the Year 2013 (IFLR Europe Awards) and Finance Team of the Year 2013 (Legal Business Awards).

The firm prides itself on bringing together exceptional lawyers from a wide range of backgrounds. This diversity stems from a firmly-held belief that different thinking translates into a competitive edge for clients. For that reason, Clifford Chance looks for graduates with drive and potential rather than a particular degree. Trainees will work hard. Focus and dedication are essential, but in return they receive all the investment and support needed to forge a compelling career. What's more, they enjoy a level of international exposure offered by only a handful of firms, and the chance to learn from some of the best minds in the legal profession.

GRADUATE VACANCIES IN 2014

LAW

NUMBER OF VACANCIES

100 graduate jobs

For training contracts starting in 2016.

LOCATIONS OF VACANCIES

STARTING SALARY FOR 2014

£39,000

UNIVERSITY VISITS IN 2013-14

ABERDEEN, BELFAST, BIRMINGHAM, BRISTOL, CAMBRIDGE, DUNDEE, DURHAM, EDINBURGH, EXETER, GLASGOW, IMPERIAL COLLEGE LONDON, KING'S COLLEGE LONDON, LEICESTER, LONDON SCHOOL OF ECONOMICS, MANCHESTER, NEWCASTLE, NOTTINGHAM, OXFORD, QUEEN MARY LONDON, READING, SCHOOL OF AFRICAN STUDIES, SHEFFIELD, SOUTHAMPTON, ST ANDREWS, TRINITY COLLEGE DUBLIN, UNIVERSITY COLLEGE DUBLIN, UNIVERSITY COLLEGE LONDON, WARWICK, YORK

Please check with your university careers service for full details of local events.

MINIMUM ENTRY REQUIREMENTS

2.1 Degree

340 UCAS points

APPLICATION DEADLINE

Law: 31st July 2014

Non-law: 31st January 2014

FURTHER INFORMATION

www.Top100GraduateEmployers.com

Register now for the latest news, events information and graduate recruitment details for Britain's leading employers.

The **co-operative**

www.co-operative.jobs

graduate.recruitment@co-operative.coop  

facebook.com/cooperativegraduateprogrammes 

As the UK's largest co-operative business and Fairtrade retailer, The Co-operative Group has almost 7 million members, a turnover of £13bn and more than 110,000 employees. Founded on pioneering ethical values, like any business they want to make a healthy profit, but in a whole new way.

The organisation combines challenging commercial targets with groundbreaking social and sustainable goals. With 14 million customers and almost 8,000 outlets, stores, funeral directors, legal services providers, distribution centres, farms and pharmacies, there's plenty for ambitious graduates to look forward to.

What sets The Co-operative apart is, well, being a co-operative. It's defined as: 'A socially responsible and ethical trading model owned and run by its members.'

The reality means so much more. It means that people enjoy the opportunity to shape how the business is run. That commercial success is invested back into its colleagues and communities. And that its ethical values are brought to life, every day, across every business area. Everything they do focuses on making a profit, that in turn, is used to make a difference.

Being ethical and fair has been at the heart of The Co-operative since they were founded in 1844 on a pioneering vision that everyone should have a say (and a share) in the business. And it still rings true today – offering opportunities for ambitious colleagues to help shape their future.

Graduates at The Co-operative continue to deliver innovative and sustainable business solutions, enjoy a vast range of career development opportunities, work with inspirational leaders and mentors and make a difference to society and their local communities.

GRADUATE VACANCIES IN 2014

RETAILING

NUMBER OF VACANCIES

To be confirmed

LOCATIONS OF VACANCIES

STARTING SALARY FOR 2014

£Competitive

UNIVERSITY VISITS IN 2013-14

CAMBRIDGE, DURHAM, LANCASTER, LEEDS, LEICESTER, LIVERPOOL, MANCHESTER, NEWCASTLE, NOTTINGHAM, NOTTINGHAM TRENT, OXFORD, SHEFFIELD

Please check with your university careers service for full details of local events.

MINIMUM ENTRY REQUIREMENTS

2.2 Degree

Relevant degree required for some roles.

APPLICATION DEADLINE

Varies by function

FURTHER INFORMATION

www.Top100GraduateEmployers.com

Register now for the latest news, events information and graduate recruitment details for Britain's leading employers.

Turn a profit -
into a better society
We're a business full of great people. People who go to great lengths to make life better for everyone. That means making a profit, of course. But as a co-operative, it's also about using our commercial success to invest in our colleagues, as well as our communities. We never rest on our laurels. We want to keep improving. And we've opportunities for even more ambitious graduates to join us.
To explore more, visit www.co-operative.jobs
The co-operative

Coca-Cola Enterprises

www.cokecce.com/careers

twitter.com/CokeCCE 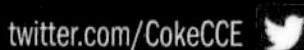

Coca-Cola Enterprises (CCE) are the world's third largest bottler of Coca-Cola products. They manufacture, sell and distribute the products of The Coca-Cola Company and selected other beverage brands in Belgium, France, Great Britain, Luxembourg, the Netherlands, Norway and Sweden.

CCE has an extensive portfolio of some of the world's best loved brands including Coca-Cola®, Fanta®, Powerade®, Glaceau vitaminwater®, Monster® and Capri-Sun®.

With an award winning CRS strategy and a legacy of sporting sponsorships, CCE provides its customers and its employees with 'only Coke can do' experiences. Their motivation is to be the best beverage sales and customer service company – and that means hiring the best.

CCE's University Talent Programmes (UTP) offers graduates an exciting range of opportunities to become business leaders of the future. Their UTP's are 3 year rotational programmes in Sales & Marketing, Finance, Supply Chain and Human Resources. Successful graduates are given the opportunity to develop and learn from their different rotations as well as being supported along the way by mentors and line managers. From their first day, graduates are put into a real role with all the responsibility and accountability that comes with it.

This type of opportunity requires a special type of graduate. So as well as being ambitious and eager to learn, CCE looks for graduates who match their values and who are accountable, team-driven and customer focussed. They look for graduates who have personalities with the power to influence and connect; graduates who can sustain the pace to keep on growing; who will make an impact and who have a desire to win.

GRADUATE VACANCIES IN 2014

- ENGINEERING
- FINANCE
- HUMAN RESOURCES
- MARKETING
- SALES

NUMBER OF VACANCIES
20+ graduate jobs

LOCATIONS OF VACANCIES

STARTING SALARY FOR 2014
£Competitive

UNIVERSITY VISITS IN 2013-14
ASTON, BATH, BIRMINGHAM, BRISTOL, EAST ANGLIA, EDINBURGH, EXETER, KING'S COLLEGE LONDON, KENT, LANCASTER, LEICESTER, LOUGHBOROUGH, MANCHESTER, NOTTINGHAM, SOUTHAMPTON, ST ANDREWS, SURREY, SUSSEX, UNIVERSITY COLLEGE LONDON, YORK
Please check with your university careers service for full details of local events.

MINIMUM ENTRY REQUIREMENTS
2.1 Degree
Relevant degree required for some roles.

APPLICATION DEADLINE
Varies by function

FURTHER INFORMATION
www.Top100GraduateEmployers.com
Register now for the latest news, events information and graduate recruitment details for Britain's leading employers.

THIRST
FOR FIRST
Leading brands, great people, growth and the reward that comes with it: the raw materials for success are right here.
But still, success depends on our graduates having the same thirst as all of our people: a thirst for exploring new territory, a thirst for pushing limits, and a thirst for the rigour and challenge of a fast-moving business.
Do you have a personality with the power to influence and connect?
Can you sustain the pace to keep on growing?
Will you make an impact with your desire to win?
Coca-Cola Enterprises
Thirst.
www.cokecce.com/careers

CREDIT SUISSE

credit-suisse.com/careers

facebook.com/creditsuissecareers

Credit Suisse is a global financial services company providing a broad range of advisory services, comprehensive solutions and excellent products through two global divisions, Private Banking & Wealth Management and Investment Banking. It serves companies, institutions and private clients around the world.

As a stable company with a long banking tradition, Credit Suisse is one of the most respected banks in the world, recognised by industry publications for its continued excellence and leading position in many key markets around the world.

Credit Suisse is active in more than 50 countries and employs over 46,000 people. Since its founding in 1856, the organisation has continuously set new standards in service and advice, and created intelligent solutions in response to changing client needs. It is renowned for its expertise and valued for its advice, innovation and execution.

Credit Suisse offers entry-level programs in a variety of business areas. The organisation's programs give graduates the chance to make a difference from day one, and provide world-class training and support to help them to develop into future business leaders. Whichever program successful candidates choose, they'll contribute to projects that have a significant impact on the business, while building their own expertise. And throughout their career with the company, graduates will benefit from cross-business and international mobility opportunities.

Credit Suisse looks for people with a wide range of experiences, interests and degrees who will add fresh perspectives to the business. The organisation's vision is to become the world's most admired bank. A graduate career with Credit Suisse can help shape the future of the organisation.

GRADUATE VACANCIES IN 2014

INVESTMENT BANKING

NUMBER OF VACANCIES

No fixed quota

LOCATIONS OF VACANCIES

Vacancies also available in Europe, Asia, the USA and elsewhere in the world.

STARTING SALARY FOR 2014

£Competitive

UNIVERSITY VISITS IN 2013-14

BIRMINGHAM, CAMBRIDGE, IMPERIAL COLLEGE LONDON, KING'S COLLEGE LONDON, LONDON SCHOOL OF ECONOMICS, MANCHESTER, OXFORD, SOUTHAMPTON, UNIVERSITY COLLEGE LONDON, WARWICK

Please check with your university careers service for full details of local events.

MINIMUM ENTRY REQUIREMENTS

2.1 Degree

APPLICATION DEADLINE

17th November 2013

FURTHER INFORMATION

www.Top100GraduateEmployers.com

Register now for the latest news, events information and graduate recruitment details for Britain's leading employers.

danone.co.uk/graduates

careeers.ukireland@danone.com

linkedin.com/company/danone/careers  facebook.com/danoneukgraduates

For over 100 years, a unique purpose to 'bring health through food and beverages to as many people as possible', has inspired world-leading brands such as Evian, Activia, Cow & Gate and Nutricia. Today, this purpose unites 102,000 Danone employees behind products that reach seven billion consumers worldwide.

The Danone graduate scheme is designed to attract motivated individuals who share Danone's passion and who demonstrate strong self-awareness, curiosity and ambition. In return, it provides them with the essential qualities needed to grow into committed and inspirational future leaders.

Although a global business, Danone has a non-hierarchical structure that ensures every employee is equally valued, respected and empowered to make a difference. For graduates, that means they are placed in influential roles, with independence and autonomy, gaining extensive experience to support their personal progression.

Individual growth and development are an integral part of the company's DNA. A graduate's learning journey is completely personalised, based on their career aspirations and developmental targets. Along the way, they are fully supported by an internal coach and a network of key individuals who are committed to helping them achieve their goals.

Danone was built on the pioneering spirit of its founders. It's their spirit that underpins the core values of the entire organisation and their legacy is the development of a business that began and remains at the forefront of innovation. Today, Danone is No.1 worldwide in fresh Dairy products, No.2 worldwide in Waters (by volume), No.2 worldwide in Baby Nutrition and No.1 in Europe in Medical Nutrition. In its graduates, Danone is looking for new and exciting visionaries to continue this legacy.

GRADUATE VACANCIES IN 2014

- FINANCE
- HUMAN RESOURCES
- LOGISTICS
- MARKETING
- RESEARCH & DEVELOPMENT
- SALES

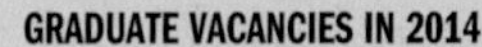

NUMBER OF VACANCIES
25-30 graduate jobs

LOCATIONS OF VACANCIES

STARTING SALARY FOR 2014
£26,500
5-10% bonus and flexible benefits.

UNIVERSITY VISITS IN 2013-14
ASTON, BATH, BIRMINGHAM, BRISTOL, CAMBRIDGE, DURHAM, EXETER, KING'S COLLEGE LONDON, LANCASTER, LONDON SCHOOL OF ECONOMICS, MANCHESTER, NOTTINGHAM, OXFORD, READING, SURREY
Please check with your university careers service for full details of local events.

MINIMUM ENTRY REQUIREMENTS
2.1 Degree
300-320 UCAS points
Dependent on programme.

APPLICATION DEADLINE
Year-round recruitment

FURTHER INFORMATION
www.Top100GraduateEmployers.com
Register now for the latest news, events information and graduate recruitment details for Britain's leading employers.

Deloitte.

www.deloitte.co.uk/graduates

gradrec@deloitte.co.uk 

twitter.com/deloitteukgrads facebook.com/yourfutureatdeloitteuk

youtube.com/deloittecareersuk linkedin.com/company/deloitte-uk

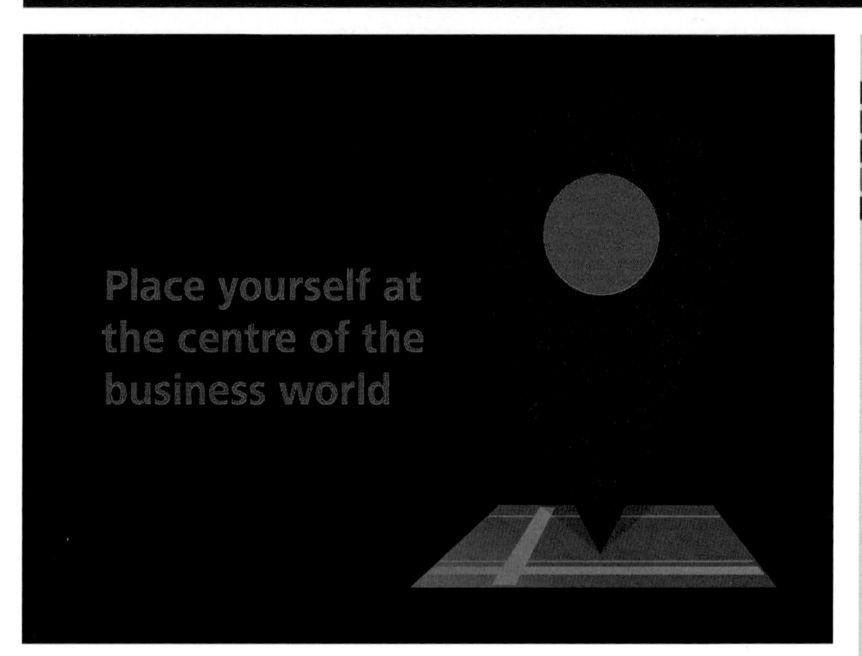
Place yourself at
the centre of the
business world

Helping the biggest businesses make some of their biggest decisions. Tackling the most complex operations. Leading the leading-edge. Developing expertise not just in one company, but in entire industries. This is what it means to be a professional at Deloitte, the world's largest professional services firm.

Deloitte offers five distinct entry routes within Audit, Tax, Consulting, Corporate Finance and Technology. Choose any of these programmes and students will enjoy an unparalleled start to their career in business, tackling a wide range of assignments with high-profile clients across different sectors; receiving coaching from senior colleagues; benefiting from world-class training and development; and working towards professional qualifications. What's more, students can expect excellent rewards and plenty of recognition for their hard work too.

For students at university, there are a huge range of opportunities on offer at Deloitte. On the graduate scheme students will spend 3 years working towards a professional qualification as well as gaining a mixture of client exposure, challenging projects and extensive training that will develop them into a fully qualified professional.

Deloitte also has work experience schemes that will give undergraduates a route into the business world few other firms can offer. Depending on what year students are in at university they can choose from the following schemes: Spring into Deloitte, Summer Vacation Scheme, Industrial Placement and Graduate scheme.

Deloitte welcome people of all backgrounds and any degree discipline. They operate on a first come, first served basis, and places are limited so they encourage students to apply as early as possible.

GRADUATE VACANCIES IN 2014

- ACCOUNTANCY
- CONSULTING
- FINANCE
- IT
- PROPERTY

NUMBER OF VACANCIES

1,200 graduate jobs

LOCATIONS OF VACANCIES

STARTING SALARY FOR 2014

£Competitive

Plus a mix of core and optional benefits.

UNIVERSITY VISITS IN 2013-14

ABERDEEN, ASTON, BATH, BIRMINGHAM, BRISTOL, CAMBRIDGE, CARDIFF, CITY, DUNDEE, DURHAM, EAST ANGLIA, EDINBURGH, EXETER, GLASGOW, HULL, IMPERIAL COLLEGE LONDON, KING'S COLLEGE LONDON, KENT, LANCASTER, LEEDS, LEICESTER, LIVERPOOL, LONDON SCHOOL OF ECONOMICS, LOUGHBOROUGH, MANCHESTER, NEWCASTLE, NORTHUMBRIA, NOTTINGHAM, NOTTINGHAM TRENT, OXFORD, OXFORD BROOKES, QUEEN MARY LONDON, READING, ROYAL HOLLOWAY LONDON, SCHOOL OF AFRICAN STUDIES, SHEFFIELD, SOUTHAMPTON, ST ANDREWS, STRATHCLYDE, SURREY, SUSSEX, ULSTER, UNIVERSITY COLLEGE LONDON, WARWICK, YORK

Please check with your university careers service for full details of local events.

MINIMUM ENTRY REQUIREMENTS

2.1 Degree

300 UCAS points

APPLICATION DEADLINE

Year-round recruitment

Early application advised.

FURTHER INFORMATION

www.Top100GraduateEmployers.com

Register now for the latest news, events information and graduate recruitment details for Britain's leading employers.

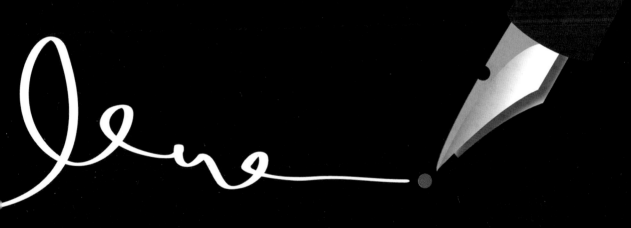

www.dfid.gov.uk/graduate

facebook.com/ukdfid graduaterecruitment@dfid.gov.uk

youtube.com/user/ukdfid twitter.com/dfid_uk

© Lindsay Mgbor/DFID

The Department for International Development (DFID) leads the UK Government's fight against world poverty. Since its creation, DFID has helped more than 250 million people lift themselves from poverty and helped 40 million more children to go to primary school. But there is still much to do.

DFID works with national and international partners to eliminate global poverty and its causes, as part of the UN 'Millennium Development Goals'. It also responds to overseas emergencies.

DFID's Graduate Development Scheme offers a diverse range of work experience in key teams across DFID, all united by a single goal: to tackle poverty and help people in developing countries improve their lives.

During the paid 50 week development placement, successful applicants will work with experienced professionals on specific projects, for example, contributing to evaluating where, when and how DFID delivers the UK's aid programme. They will take on a role suited to their skills, experience and career aims, in one of a number of areas, including: research and evaluation; Africa policy and development; conflict, humanitarian crisis and security; European Union policy; United Nations and Commonwealth policy; youth development and policy; health; Finance, H.R. and I.T.

DFID is committed to supporting all staff to realise their potential. When graduates join DFID, they will have a structured development programme designed to help them learn and contribute as quickly as possible. Their personal development plan will include training and prominent speaker events, e-learning, a mentor and dedicated time for reflection and peer-to-peer learning.

DFID is an equal opportunities employer, welcoming applications from all parts of the community.

GRADUATE VACANCIES IN 2014

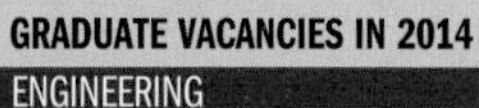

- ENGINEERING
- FINANCE
- GENERAL MANAGEMENT
- HUMAN RESOURCES
- IT
- PURCHASING
- RESEARCH & DEVELOPMENT

NUMBER OF VACANCIES
50 graduate jobs

LOCATIONS OF VACANCIES

STARTING SALARY FOR 2014
£22,000

UNIVERSITY VISITS IN 2013-14
Please check with your university careers service for full details of local events.

MINIMUM ENTRY REQUIREMENTS
2.1 Degree

APPLICATION DEADLINE
25th February 2014

FURTHER INFORMATION
www.Top100GraduateEmployers.com
Register now for the latest news, events information and graduate recruitment details for Britain's leading employers.

www.diageo.com/careers

globalcareers@diageo.com

twitter.com/diageoplc facebook.com/diageoeuropeangraduates

youtube.com/diageocareers linkedin.com/company/diageo

As the world's leading premium drinks company, Diageo knows the value of a good idea. It's how they got to where they are today. And with their relentless pursuit of new ideas and their unwavering focus on innovation, it's how they'll build on their rich heritage – and enjoy even greater success tomorrow.

Diageo has an exceptional portfolio of beverage alcohol brands – Baileys, Captain Morgan, Guinness and Smirnoff to name but a few. They employ 28,000 people in 80 countries. All with one aim: to help millions of people celebrate life every day, everywhere.

Diageo celebrates success. Through its unique culture involving close collaboration and true team spirit, the company prides itself on achieving things others can't.

Successful applicants to Diageo's graduate programmes and undergraduate summer internships will be bright, curious and passionate. Some will have an entrepreneurial spirit for sales or a creative flair for consumer marketing. Others will find their niche in finance, human resources, manufacturing or supply chain and logistics. Diageo looks for people who are authentic in what they do and can demonstrate high levels of integrity. Equally as important, they need people who are brimming with ideas, and who can bring those ideas to life.

Every graduate is given outstanding training and real challenges from day one – preparing them to become future leaders, with support from a dedicated buddy and mentor. Being a truly global company, Diageo also offers opportunities to work in different parts of the world.

As expected, Diageo promotes a happy work/life balance and provides a competitive salary with great benefits to help their graduates live life to the full. It's no wonder they're among the world's most admired companies to work for.

GRADUATE VACANCIES IN 2014
- ENGINEERING
- FINANCE
- HUMAN RESOURCES
- MARKETING
- SALES

NUMBER OF VACANCIES
50 graduate jobs

LOCATIONS OF VACANCIES

Vacancies also available in Europe.

STARTING SALARY FOR 2014
£Competitive

UNIVERSITY VISITS IN 2013-14
BATH, BELFAST, DURHAM, EDINBURGH, EXETER, LANCASTER, LEEDS, LOUGHBOROUGH, NEWCASTLE, NOTTINGHAM, OXFORD, STRATHCLYDE, TRINITY COLLEGE DUBLIN, UNIVERSITY COLLEGE DUBLIN, WARWICK
Please check with your university careers service for full details of local events.

MINIMUM ENTRY REQUIREMENTS
2.1 Degree
300 UCAS points

APPLICATION DEADLINE
Year-round recruitment
Early application advised.

FURTHER INFORMATION
www.Top100GraduateEmployers.com
Register now for the latest news, events information and graduate recruitment details for Britain's leading employers.

www.dlapipergraduates.co.uk

facebook.com/dlapiperukgraduates
recruitment.graduate@dlapiper.com
linkedin.com/pub/dla-piper-graduates/4b/b38/a93
twitter.com/DLA_Piper_News

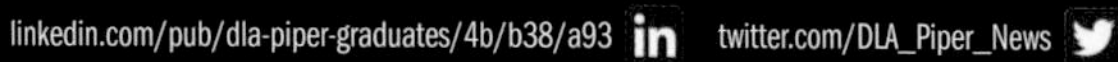

DLA Piper is a global law firm with 4,200 lawyers located in more than 30 countries throughout the Americas, Asia Pacific, Europe and the Middle East, positioning them to help companies with their legal needs anywhere in the world. Their vision is to be the leading global business law firm.

The firm's success depends on its people and a progressive approach to recruitment has delivered a mix of talents which has contributed to this success. They want to inspire their people and help them to develop commercial and business skills, whilst having a positive impact on local communities.

It is essential for the success of their business that they recruit the strongest graduates, who will not only deliver technical excellence, but also exceptional client service. To achieve this they need a diverse group of talented individuals who have a consistently strong academic performance, formidable commercial acumen, who are articulate, ambitious, driven and dynamic with sharp minds, enthusiasm and intellectual curiosity.

Once they join the firm, trainees complete four six-month seats and are given an opportunity to express what areas of law they would like to experience during their training contracts. There are also opportunities to do a seat abroad, or a client secondment.

Trainees who want responsibility, and display the right level of aptitude, will be given as much as they can handle. This refreshing approach to learning and development, combined with an open door policy, provides trainees with an excellent foundation on which to build their careers. The firm's award winning training programme ensures that their people are developed throughout their time at DLA Piper, as they believe in investing in the careers and reputation of their people.

GRADUATE VACANCIES IN 2014

LAW

NUMBER OF VACANCIES

80 graduate jobs

For training contracts starting in 2016.

LOCATIONS OF VACANCIES

STARTING SALARY FOR 2014

£22,000-£37,000

UNIVERSITY VISITS IN 2013-14

BIRMINGHAM, BRISTOL, CAMBRIDGE, CITY UNIVERSITY LONDON, DURHAM, EDINBURGH, GLASGOW, KING'S COLLEGE LONDON, LANCASTER, LEEDS, LIVERPOOL, LONDON SCHOOL OF ECONOMICS, MANCHESTER, NEWCASTLE, NOTTINGHAM, OXFORD, QUEEN MARY LONDON, SHEFFIELD, SOUTHAMPTON, UNIVERSITY COLLEGE LONDON, WARWICK, YORK

Please check with your university careers service for full details of local events.

MINIMUM ENTRY REQUIREMENTS

2.1 Degree

320 UCAS points

APPLICATION DEADLINE

Law: 31st July 2014

Non-law: 31st July 2014

FURTHER INFORMATION

www.Top100GraduateEmployers.com

Register now for the latest news, events information and graduate recruitment details for Britain's leading employers.

BIGGER

OPPORTUNITIES

DLA Piper offers big opportunities to ambitious graduates – big firm, big clients, big careers.

Don't just take our word for it. Find out more at www.dlapipergraduates.co.uk

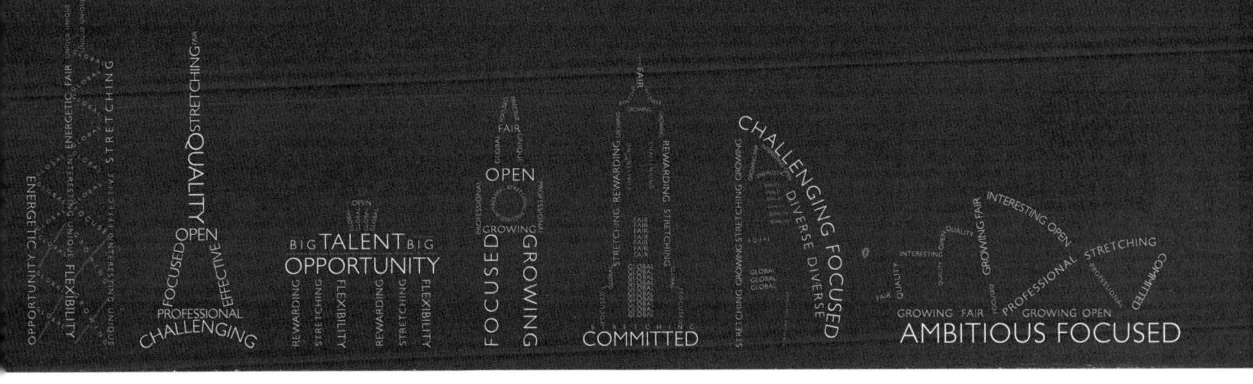

www.edfenergy.com/graduates

linkedin.com/company/edf-energy/careers futurecapability@edfenergy.com

In the years to come, the energy industry will face some of its greatest challenges. Climate change, security of supply, the need for new infrastructure – all of these will affect the way things are done. But as the largest generator of low-carbon electricity in the UK, EDF Energy is perfectly placed to tackle such issues.

The graduates taken on now will help them to do just that; harnessing the potential of nuclear power to make a sustainable energy future a reality. It's a challenge. But more than that, it's a unique opportunity for graduates to gain the skills, experience and confidence they need to build a great career and to play a part in defining the UK energy industry for generations to come.

From civil, electrical, mechanical and chemical engineering; physics, chemistry and mathematics; finance, marketing, HR, supply chain and business analysis; every one of their graduate schemes offers a structured programme with a variety of placements.

They're schemes designed to support, test and develop people who have the potential to be future industry leaders and to offer some of the most technically challenging, professionally inspiring, personally rewarding opportunities imaginable. All programmes feature a benefits package that is designed to match individual talents and reward contribution to the business.

With expertise in a wide range of energy sources and across many stages of the energy process, theirs is a unique proposition. One that will set the path to a bright and rewarding future and redefine the UK Energy Industry, shaping it for generations to come. Together with their commitment to reducing the intensity of CO_2 emissions from electricity production to 60% and helping the UK meet its target of 80% reductions in CO_2 by 2050, it is a challenge like no other.

GRADUATE VACANCIES IN 2014

- ENGINEERING
- FINANCE
- HUMAN RESOURCES
- MARKETING

NUMBER OF VACANCIES

60 graduate jobs

LOCATIONS OF VACANCIES

STARTING SALARY FOR 2014

£25,000-£26,500

Circa 5% bonus via the Company Incentive Plan.

UNIVERSITY VISITS IN 2013-14

BIRMINGHAM, IMPERIAL COLLEGE LONDON, LEICESTER, LOUGHBOROUGH, MANCHESTER, STRATHCLYDE, UNIVERSITY COLLEGE LONDON

Please check with your university careers service for full details of local events.

MINIMUM ENTRY REQUIREMENTS

2.1 Degree

Relevant degree required for some roles.

APPLICATION DEADLINE

January 2014

FURTHER INFORMATION

www.Top100GraduateEmployers.com

Register now for the latest news, events information and graduate recruitment details for Britain's leading employers.

So, are you a big splash or a small ripple kind of person?
Exceptional opportunities for graduates from all disciplines.
It's time to push yourself further. To apply fresh thinking. To define the UK energy industry for generations to come. Perhaps you're up for the engineering challenge of building our nuclear future. Or maybe the commercial, logistical and human aspects of managing a fast-growing business are more your thing. It's all waiting for you to jump straight in at EDF Energy.
Find out more at edfenergy.com/graduates
eDF
ENERGY

www.eu-careers.eu

twitter.com/EU_Careers  facebook.com/EU.Careers.EPSO

youtube.com/user/EUCareers linkedin.com/company/3040469

Looking for a challenging career in a dynamic environment? Based in the heart of Europe, the EU Institutions offer a truly international career to ambitious and capable graduates. Serving 500 million citizens, a range of career choices are on offer, all with the chance to make a real and lasting difference.

For final year students and graduates, entry-level positions are available in various fields, from law, to economics, or languages, as well as more general policy or project management roles. New recruits could be drafting legislation, helping to implement EU law, developing communication strategies, or managing projects and resources.

Most positions are based either in Brussels or Luxembourg, with around 20% of staff based in offices throughout the world. Applying for an EU Career could in practice mean working for the European Commission, the Council of the EU, the European Parliament, the European External Action Service, the European Court of Justice, the Court of Auditors, or any of the other main EU Institutions or Agencies.

Interested applicants will need to prove their strong analytical, organisational and communication skills, a drive to deliver the best possible results, the ability to work effectively as part of a multi-cultural team, and a potential for leadership and personal development.

Candidates are selected through a process of open competition, which generally consists of a first round of computer-based tests in centres throughout the EU, followed by an assessment centre in Brussels or Luxembourg for the best performers. The main graduate recruitment cycle normally opens in the spring, but all of the EU Institutions offer paid graduate traineeships throughout the year – a great way to gain a first taste of a future EU career.

GRADUATE VACANCIES IN 2014

- FINANCE
- GENERAL MANAGEMENT
- HUMAN RESOURCES
- IT
- LAW
- MARKETING
- MEDIA
- RESEARCH & DEVELOPMENT

NUMBER OF VACANCIES
No fixed quota

LOCATIONS OF VACANCIES

Vacancies available in Europe.

STARTING SALARY FOR 2014
£41,500+

UNIVERSITY VISITS IN 2013-14
BATH, CAMBRIDGE, CARDIFF, DURHAM, EDINBURGH, KING'S COLLEGE LONDON, KENT, LEICESTER, NEWCASTLE, OXFORD, SHEFFIELD, ST ANDREWS, WARWICK, YORK
Please check with your university careers service for full details of local events.

MINIMUM ENTRY REQUIREMENTS
Relevant degree required for some roles.

APPLICATION DEADLINE
Varies by function

FURTHER INFORMATION
www.Top100GraduateEmployers.com
Register now for the latest news, events information and graduate recruitment details for Britain's leading employers.

EY
Building a better
working world

ey.com/uk/careers

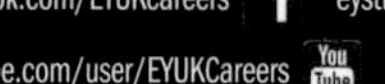

facebook.com/EYUKcareers
eystudentrecruitment@uk.ey.com
youtube.com/user/EYUKCareers
twitter.com/EY_StudentsUK

EY is one of the world's leading professional services firms. It has 167,000 people in 140 countries, with combined global revenues of US $24.4 billion and plans to be a $50 billion organisation by 2020. It seeks driven, ambitious graduates who want a stimulating and challenging start to their careers.

EY's clients are some of the most successful, innovative and respected global organisations, and range across all industry and public sectors. EY people understand how businesses work. Their ingenuity, dynamism and creativity help anticipate and meet their clients' needs: improving how they work, grow, seize opportunities, and make vital business decisions about the future of the working world. They work in four service lines across the world: Advisory, Assurance, Corporate Finance and Tax.

EY prides itself on its world-class training, mentoring and professional qualifications – the first step to a successful, varied and fulfilling career path. The firm offers on-campus workshops with guidance about applications, interviews and provides useful advice on how to increase employability. Inspiring talks and sessions offer insights into the business world to help graduates improve their commercial awareness.

Students are encouraged to apply to one of the EY undergraduate programmes, designed to discover their natural strengths and forge a career that takes them as far as they want to go. And with an internship or placement, candidates will engage directly with global organisations on real projects while learning what working life is like at EY.

Careers at the top of the business world are defined by where they start. Starting at EY gives the skills, contacts and experiences to make a career go further, faster.

GRADUATE VACANCIES IN 2014

- ACCOUNTANCY
- CONSULTING
- FINANCE
- IT

NUMBER OF VACANCIES
700 graduate jobs

LOCATIONS OF VACANCIES

Vacancies also available in Europe.

STARTING SALARY FOR 2014
£Competitive

UNIVERSITY VISITS IN 2013-14
ABERDEEN, ASTON, BATH, BIRMINGHAM, BRISTOL, CAMBRIDGE, CARDIFF, CITY, DURHAM, EDINBURGH, EXETER, GLASGOW, IMPERIAL COLLEGE LONDON, KING'S COLLEGE LONDON, LANCASTER, LEEDS, LONDON SCHOOL OF ECONOMICS, LOUGHBOROUGH, MANCHESTER, NEWCASTLE, NOTTINGHAM, OXFORD, READING, SHEFFIELD, SOUTHAMPTON, ST ANDREWS, STRATHCLYDE, SURREY, UNIVERSITY COLLEGE LONDON, WARWICK, YORK
Please check with your university careers service for full details of local events.

MINIMUM ENTRY REQUIREMENTS
2.1 Degree
300 UCAS points

APPLICATION DEADLINE
Year-round recruitment
Early application advised.

FURTHER INFORMATION
www.Top100GraduateEmployers.com
Register now for the latest news, events information and graduate recruitment details for Britain's leading employers.

EY
Building a better working world
GO FURTHER, FASTER.
EY graduates like Jon are part of a global organisation advising big businesses on issues critical to their long-term success.
If you have the ambition, EY will give you the training and experiences you need to help grow our global business and build a better working world.
To find out more about opportunities at EY, visit ey.com/uk/careers.
© 2013 Ernst & Young LLP. All Rights Reserved.

www.freshfields.com/uktrainees

facebook.com/FreshfieldsUkTrainees f uktrainees@freshfields.com

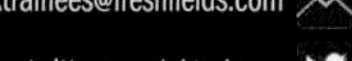

youtube.com/Freshfieldsfilm twitter.com/uktrainees

As an international law firm, Freshfields Bruckhaus Deringer advises some of the world's most well known businesses. For graduates keen to pursue a career in commercial law, the firm offers challenging work that demands a strong intellect and a desire to help ambitious businesses achieve long-term success.

The firm provides clients with a global service from its network of offices across Europe, the Americas and Asia. It is essential that this service is consistent and of the highest quality.

Graduates who accept a training contract with the firm have the opportunity to experience up to eight areas of law – twice the number offered by most law firms. The training is largely provided from the firm's London office but many trainees will also spend time on secondment to a client or to one of the firm's US, European or Asian offices.

The lawyers work in teams, often of no more than three: a partner, an associate and a trainee. Whatever clients want to achieve, the team's job is to work out how. Is it possible? What will be the most effective way of structuring the deal or tackling the problem? What are the risks? How should it be documented? The team has to provide real commercial solutions, not just what is right or wrong in law.

Background, university, and the degree studied are immaterial. But every successful candidate has three qualities that are non-negotiable: intellectual talent, excellent English (written and verbal), and a generous spirit.

The firm pursues premium, cross-border work that is nearly always complicated. This means that the learning curve is steep, so the graduates who do best are those who like to be challenged.

GRADUATE VACANCIES IN 2014

LAW

NUMBER OF VACANCIES

90 graduate jobs

For training contracts starting in 2016.

LOCATIONS OF VACANCIES

STARTING SALARY FOR 2014

£39,000

UNIVERSITY VISITS IN 2013-14

ABERDEEN, ASTON, BELFAST, BIRMINGHAM, BRISTOL, CAMBRIDGE, CARDIFF, CITY, DURHAM, EAST ANGLIA, EDINBURGH, ESSEX, EXETER, GLASGOW, KING'S COLLEGE, KENT, LANCASTER, LEEDS, LEICESTER, LIVERPOOL, LONDON SCHOOL OF ECONOMICS, MANCHESTER, NEWCASTLE, NORTHUMBRIA, NOTTINGHAM, OXFORD, QUEEN MARY LONDON, READING, SHEFFIELD, SOUTHAMPTON, ST ANDREWS, TRINITY COLLEGE DUBLIN, UNIVERSITY COLLEGE DUBLIN, UNIVERSITY COLLEGE LONDON, WARWICK, YORK

Please check with your university careers service for full details of local events.

APPLICATION DEADLINE

Law: 31st July 2014

Non-law: 6th January 2014

FURTHER INFORMATION

www.Top100GraduateEmployers.com

Register now for the latest news, events information and graduate recruitment details for Britain's leading employers.

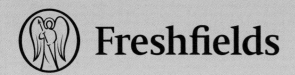

www.ge.com/uk/careers

twitter.com/GECareers facebook.com/gecareers
youtube.com/user/GE  linkedin.com/company/ge/careers

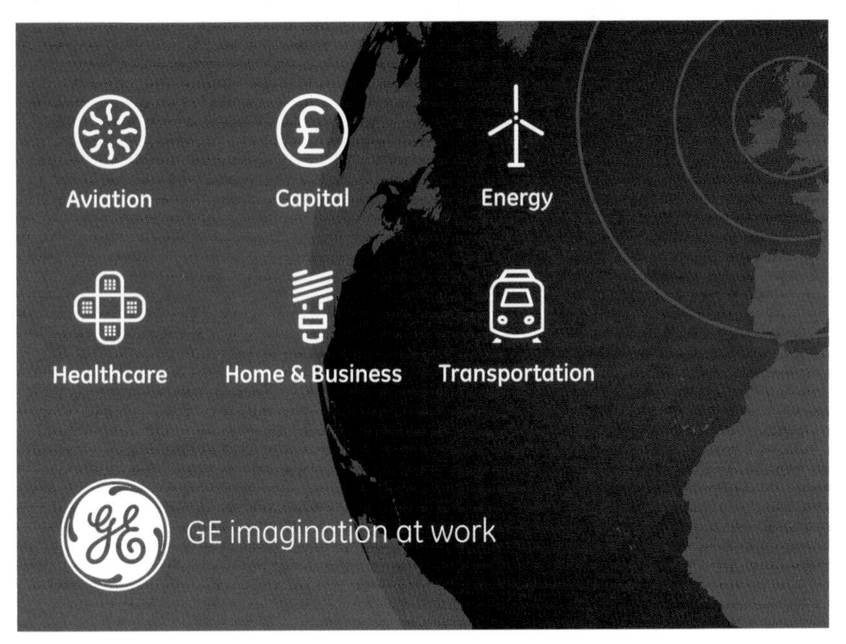

Founded by Thomas Edison in 1878, GE is one of the world's biggest and most valuable brands, operating in over 100 countries and employing 300,000 people worldwide. In the UK alone, GE employs over 18,000 people across 60 major locations.

GE has a long history of invention and innovation with a diverse portfolio – from financial services and power generation, to aircraft engines and healthcare. Its employees work on things that matter by building, powering, moving and curing the world. Today, GE Technology will help doctors save 3,000 lives; a GE powered aircraft will take off every two seconds; GE Capital will provide $1.5 billion in credit for businesses and GE Energy will create 25% of the world's electricity.

Those who are successful in joining GE would become part of a dynamic and talented global workforce, consistently rated No 1 for leadership. It is a company where graduates have unique opportunities to learn, to develop and to establish fantastic careers.

GE offers a variety of internships and graduate programmes covering engineering, operations, research and development, IT, finance, HR and marketing. The company seeks to attract those who are passionate, clear thinkers and who work collaboratively to solve some of the world's most challenging problems.

Graduates will gain exposure to some of the world's best business leaders, expand their global mind-set and develop a diverse network of colleagues. Development is through job assignments, classroom, e-learning and mentoring. It can also include opportunities to travel abroad to work in one of GE's 100 locations around the world.

GRADUATE VACANCIES IN 2014
ACCOUNTANCY
ENGINEERING
FINANCE
HUMAN RESOURCES
IT
MARKETING
SALES

NUMBER OF VACANCIES
50 graduate jobs

LOCATIONS OF VACANCIES

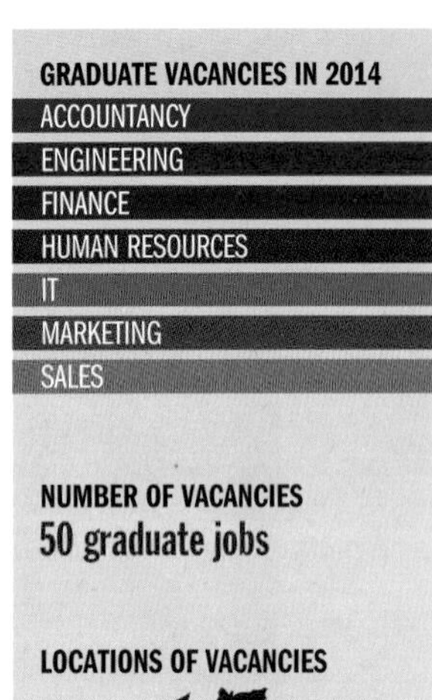

Vacancies also available in Europe, Asia, the USA and elsewhere in the world.

STARTING SALARY FOR 2014
£Competitive
Flexible benefits package.

UNIVERSITY VISITS IN 2013-14
ASTON, BATH, BRISTOL, CARDIFF, LOUGHBOROUGH, PLYMOUTH, SOUTHAMPTON, STRATHCLYDE, SWANSEA
Please check with your university careers service for full details of local events.

MINIMUM ENTRY REQUIREMENTS
Relevant degree required for some roles.

APPLICATION DEADLINE
Varies by function

FURTHER INFORMATION
www.Top100GraduateEmployers.com
Register now for the latest news, events information and graduate recruitment details for Britain's leading employers.

2005
2005

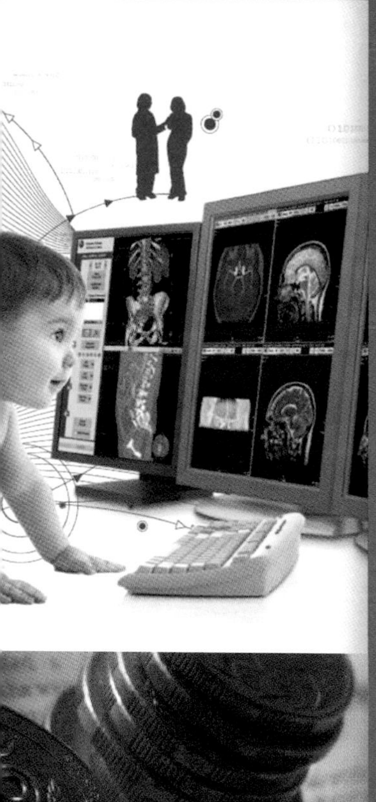

One of the world's leading healthcare companies, GSK gives its people the chance to answer some of the planet's biggest questions. Questions about future healthcare needs and about building an innovative, global business to meet them, as well as questions about their personal and professional growth.

Dedicated to helping millions of people around the world to do more, feel better and live longer, GSK is revolutionising its business to meet changing healthcare needs from London to Lima, Lusaka, Luzhou and Lahore. GSK invested £4 billion in R&D in 2012 and topped the Access to Medicine Index, underlining its commitment to tackle some of the world's deadliest diseases by embracing new, open and innovative ways of working.

GSK discover, develop, manufacture and distribute vaccines, prescription medicines and consumer health products. Based in the UK, with operations in over 100 countries, GSK produce a huge range of healthcare products from lifesaving prescription medicines and vaccines to popular consumer products like Maximuscle, Sensodyne, Aquafresh and Panadol. In fact, every year GSK screen about 65 million compounds, make over four billion packs of medicines and healthcare products, and supply one quarter of the world's vaccines.

GSK is deeply committed to developing people through a range of ongoing development opportunities that includes tailored, 2-3 year rotational graduate programmes and industrial or summer placements. So it offers graduates the trust and respect to be themselves, and develop their careers across an incredibly diverse collection of businesses and geographies, in an environment where personal growth can play a vital part in the changing face of the business.

Most of all, GSK graduates enjoy the sense of purpose that comes from leading change in an industry that touches millions every day.

GRADUATE VACANCIES IN 2014

- ENGINEERING
- FINANCE
- HUMAN RESOURCES
- IT
- MARKETING
- RESEARCH & DEVELOPMENT
- SALES

NUMBER OF VACANCIES
50+ graduate jobs

LOCATIONS OF VACANCIES

STARTING SALARY FOR 2014
£Competitive

UNIVERSITY VISITS IN 2013-14
ASTON, CAMBRIDGE, DURHAM, EXETER, IMPERIAL COLLEGE LONDON, LOUGHBOROUGH, MANCHESTER, NOTTINGHAM, OXFORD, UNIVERSITY COLLEGE LONDON, WARWICK
Please check with your university careers service for full details of local events.

MINIMUM ENTRY REQUIREMENTS
2.1 Degree
Relevant degree required for some roles.

APPLICATION DEADLINE
Year-round recruitment
Early application advised.

FURTHER INFORMATION
www.Top100GraduateEmployers.com
Register now for the latest news, events information and graduate recruitment details for Britain's leading employers.

Goldman Sachs

www.goldmansachs.com/careers

twitter.com/GoldmanSachs  gscampusrecruitingld1@ln.email.gs.com

youtube.com/goldmansachs  linkedin.com/company/goldman-sachs/careers

The Goldman Sachs Group, Inc. is a leading global investment banking, securities and investment management firm that provides a wide range of financial services to a substantial and diversified client base that includes corporations, financial institutions, governments and high-net-worth individuals.

The people of Goldman Sachs share a passion for achieving results and recognise that success comes with integrity. Their unique backgrounds, individual perspectives and diverse skills are put to the test as they help the firm's clients achieve their business goals.

Goldman Sachs is structured in a series of divisions: Executive Office, Finance, Global Compliance, Global Investment Research, Human Capital Management, Internal Audit, Investment Banking, Investment Management, Legal, Merchant Banking, Operations, Securities, Services and Technology.

Nearly everyone – from the most senior leaders to junior analysts – is actively involved in recruiting as the goal is to recruit people who share the firm's core values. Academic achievement is important, but is only one indication of a person's potential.

Goldman Sachs recognises a diverse workforce encourages increased creativity and innovation. Diversity is crucial to improved performance and continued business success. To that end, the firm is committed to an environment that values diversity and promotes inclusion.

Academic discipline is less important to Goldman Sachs than the personal qualities an individual brings with them, however a strong interest in and appreciation of finance is important. Whatever the background may be, it is intellect, personality and zest for life that the company values the most.

GRADUATE VACANCIES IN 2014

- ACCOUNTANCY
- FINANCE
- HUMAN RESOURCES
- INVESTMENT BANKING
- IT

NUMBER OF VACANCIES

300 graduate jobs

LOCATIONS OF VACANCIES

STARTING SALARY FOR 2014

£Competitive

UNIVERSITY VISITS IN 2013-14

BATH, BIRMINGHAM, BRISTOL, CAMBRIDGE, CITY, DURHAM, EDINBURGH, GLASGOW, IMPERIAL COLLEGE LONDON, KING'S COLLEGE LONDON, LONDON SCHOOL OF ECONOMICS, LOUGHBOROUGH, MANCHESTER, NOTTINGHAM, OXFORD, SOUTHAMPTON, TRINITY COLLEGE DUBLIN, UNIVERSITY COLLEGE DUBLIN, UNIVERSITY COLLEGE LONDON, WARWICK, YORK

Please check with your university careers service for full details of local events.

APPLICATION DEADLINE

3rd November 2013

FURTHER INFORMATION

www.Top100GraduateEmployers.com

Register now for the latest news, events information and graduate recruitment details for Britain's leading employers.

www.google.com/students/emea

plus.google.com/+GoogleStudents

twitter.com/googlestudents  facebook.com/GoogleStudents

youtube.com/user/GoogleStudents 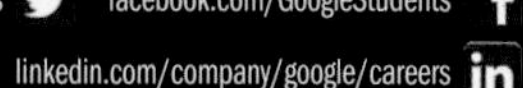

Founders Larry Page and Sergey Brin met at Stanford University in 1995. By 1996, they had built a search engine that used links to determine the importance of individual web pages. Today, Google is a tech company that helps businesses of all kinds succeed on and off the web.

It's really the people that make Google the kind of company it is. Google hire people who are smart and determined, and favour ability over experience.

New grads joining Google will enter either the Small-to-Medium Business (SMB) Sales or Global Customer Services Teams. As small business experts, Googlers in SMB help to get local entrepreneurs on the map, and deliver a beautifully simple, intuitive experience that enables customers to grow their businesses. By spotting and analysing customer needs and trends, Google's innovative teams of strategists, account developers and customer support specialists work together on scalable solutions for each business, no matter its age or size.

Google hires graduates from all disciplines, from humanities and business related courses to engineering and computer science. The ideal candidate is someone who can demonstrate a passion for the online industry and someone who has made the most of their time at university through involvement in clubs, societies or relevant internships. Google hires graduates who have a variety of strengths and passions, not just isolated skill sets. For technical roles within engineering teams, specific skills will be required.

The Google Business Associate Programme is a two-year developmental programme that supplements a Googler's core role in SMB. It offers world-class training, equipping new joiners with the business, analytical and leadership skills needed to be successful at Google.

GRADUATE VACANCIES IN 2014

- CONSULTING
- ENGINEERING
- HUMAN RESOURCES
- IT
- MARKETING
- MEDIA
- SALES

NUMBER OF VACANCIES
No fixed quota

LOCATIONS OF VACANCIES

Vacancies also available in Europe, Asia and the USA.

STARTING SALARY FOR 2014
£Competitive
Plus world-renowned perks and benefits.

UNIVERSITY VISITS IN 2013-14
Please check with your university careers service for full details of local events.

MINIMUM ENTRY REQUIREMENTS
2.1 Degree

APPLICATION DEADLINE
Year-round recruitment

FURTHER INFORMATION
www.Top100GraduateEmployers.com
Register now for the latest news, events information and graduate recruitment details for Britain's leading employers.

www.grant-thornton.co.uk/trainees

facebook.com/GrantThorntonRecruitmentUK  traineerecruitment@uk.gt.com 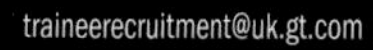

youtube.com/GrantThorntonUKGraduates 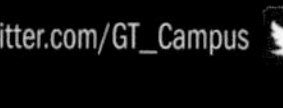 twitter.com/GT_Campus

How to sum up a complex and exciting business like Grant Thornton? Simply put, they're part of a global organisation delivering audit, tax and advisory services to dynamic organisations in over 100 countries. In the UK alone, they deliver solutions to 40,000 clients, across a wide range of sectors.

Getting right to the core of client needs and meeting them with agility and insight is at the heart of their business. In today's competitive market, this blend of expertise and personal attention is what sets them apart.

Over 300 ambitious graduates, interns and placement students join Grant Thornton in over 20 of its 27 UK offices each year. They enjoy variety and responsibility from the start on exciting client assignments, from multinationals to fast-growth companies such as start-ups. The learning curve is steep. Trainees can be leading their own team or portfolio by their second year. And with the firm's global reach there are plenty of opportunities for international exposure to clients and secondments.

The structured training, varied on-the-ground client experience and supportive working environment gives trainees the chance to develop and grow as trusted advisers with a deep understanding of business, as well as achieving a respected professional qualification and a competitive salary.

So who are they looking for? People with a passion for business, who combine technical thinking with their own instinct to give the kind of advice that makes a real difference to the organisations they work with. Grant Thornton's business advisers listen critically, dig deeper and have the confidence to challenge assumptions right from day one. They know it's about more than just the numbers, it's about enjoying tough challenges, seeking out opportunities and adding real value to clients by unlocking their potential for growth.

GRADUATE VACANCIES IN 2014

ACCOUNTANCY

NUMBER OF VACANCIES

300+ graduate jobs

LOCATIONS OF VACANCIES

STARTING SALARY FOR 2014

£Competitive

UNIVERSITY VISITS IN 2013-14

ASTON, BATH, BELFAST, BIRMINGHAM, BRISTOL, CAMBRIDGE, CARDIFF, DURHAM, EAST ANGLIA, EDINBURGH, GLASGOW, IMPERIAL COLLEGE LONDON, KING'S COLLEGE LONDON, LEEDS, LEICESTER, LIVERPOOL, LONDON SCHOOL OF ECONOMICS, LOUGHBOROUGH, MANCHESTER, NEWCASTLE, NOTTINGHAM, OXFORD, PLYMOUTH, READING, SHEFFIELD, SOUTHAMPTON, STRATHCLYDE, UNIVERSITY COLLEGE LONDON, WARWICK, YORK

Please check with your university careers service for full details of local events.

MINIMUM ENTRY REQUIREMENTS

Strong academic performance essential.

APPLICATION DEADLINE

Year-round recruitment

Early application advised.

FURTHER INFORMATION

www.Top100GraduateEmployers.com

Register now for the latest news, events information and graduate recruitment details for Britain's leading employers.

THINK TWICE
BEFORE YOU
FRIEND
YOUR BOSS
What will your advice be?

Some advice just states the obvious. But to give the kind of advice that's going to make a real difference to your clients and your career, you've got to listen critically and be credible and confident enough to make suggestions right from day one. You'll enjoy tough challenges, seek out opportunities and be ready to kick start a career as a trusted business adviser working alongside our dynamic clients. Sound like you? Here's our advice: visit...

www.grant-thornton.co.uk/graduates

Grant Thornton

An instinct for growth™

herbertsmithfreehills.com/careers/london/graduates

facebook.com/HSFgraduatesUK graduatesuk@hsf.com 

youtube.com/HSFlegal  twitter.com/HSFgraduatesUK

Herbert Smith Freehills is a global force with a market leading position in Asia Pacific. With 2,800 lawyers in offices spanning Asia, Australia, Europe, the Middle East and the US, the firm is the eighth largest law firm in the world and working across borders is at the heart of its philosophy.

The firm is committed to excellence, providing tailored legal advice of the highest quality to major corporations, governments, financial institutions and all types of commercial organisation.

Herbert Smith Freehills' disputes practice is acknowledged as the number one in the UK and Asia and includes the firm's leading international arbitration practice and award winning in-house advocacy unit, offering a complete litigation service and a realistic alternative to the bar. The firm is a market leader in corporate with a particular strength in the energy sector. Allied to this is a deep vein of quality that runs through its other practice areas including finance, competition, regulation and trade, real estate and employment, pensions and incentives. The firm also has specialist areas such as intellectual property and tax.

The training contract balances contentious and non-contentious work, pro bono opportunities, early responsibility and support. Trainees rotate around four six-month seats and are encouraged to go on secondment to a client or one of the firm's international offices.

Herbert Smith Freehills seeks to recruit people with the desire to be exceptional lawyers. As well as a solid academic record, applicants should have a strong level of commercial awareness and understand the importance of building relationships with clients and colleagues. The firm chooses people who are assured, perceptive, ambitious and empathetic. Combine these qualities with a creative and questioning mind and Herbert Smith Freehills will offer great challenges and rewards.

GRADUATE VACANCIES IN 2014

LAW

NUMBER OF VACANCIES

70 graduate jobs

For training contracts starting in 2016.

LOCATIONS OF VACANCIES

STARTING SALARY FOR 2014

£39,000

Full LPC and GDL fees, and £6,000 maintenance grant (£5,000 if studying GDL outside London).

UNIVERSITY VISITS IN 2013-14

BELFAST, BIRMINGHAM, BRISTOL, CAMBRIDGE, CARDIFF, CITY, DURHAM, EDINBURGH, EXETER, GLASGOW, IMPERIAL COLLEGE LONDON, KING'S COLLEGE LONDON, LEEDS, LEICESTER, LONDON SCHOOL OF ECONOMICS, MANCHESTER, NEWCASTLE, NOTTINGHAM, OXFORD, QUEEN MARY LONDON, READING, SHEFFIELD, SOUTHAMPTON, ST ANDREWS, STRATHCLYDE, UNIVERSITY COLLEGE LONDON, WARWICK, YORK

Please check with your university careers service for full details of local events.

MINIMUM ENTRY REQUIREMENTS

2.1 Degree

APPLICATION DEADLINE

Please see website for full details.

FURTHER INFORMATION

www.Top100GraduateEmployers.com

Register now for the latest news, events information and graduate recruitment details for Britain's leading employers.

Hogan Lovells

www.hoganlovells.com/graduates

facebook.com/hoganlovellsgradsUK  recruit@hoganlovells.com 

GRADUATE VACANCIES IN 2014

LAW

NUMBER OF VACANCIES

Up to 60 graduate jobs

For training contracts starting in 2016.

LOCATIONS OF VACANCIES

STARTING SALARY FOR 2014

£39,000

UNIVERSITY VISITS IN 2013-14

BELFAST, BIRMINGHAM, BRISTOL, CAMBRIDGE, CARDIFF, DURHAM, EDINBURGH, EXETER, IMPERIAL COLLEGE LONDON, KING'S COLLEGE LONDON, LEEDS, LONDON SCHOOL OF ECONOMICS, MANCHESTER, NEWCASTLE, NOTTINGHAM, OXFORD, SHEFFIELD, SOUTHAMPTON, ST ANDREWS, TRINITY COLLEGE DUBLIN, UNIVERSITY COLLEGE LONDON, WARWICK, YORK

Please check with your university careers service for full details of local events.

MINIMUM ENTRY REQUIREMENTS

2.1 Degree

APPLICATION DEADLINE

Law: 31st July 2014

Non-law: 31st March 2014

FURTHER INFORMATION

www.Top100GraduateEmployers.com

Register now for the latest news, events information and graduate recruitment details for Britain's leading employers.

Hogan Lovells is a top global law firm, with over 2,500 lawyers working in over 40 offices around the world. Their unique balance of ambition and approachability attracts prestigious clients and creates a working culture that ensures support and success for trainee solicitors.

Known for their global diversity and wide range of practice areas, Hogan Lovells has a strong reputation for corporate, finance, dispute resolution, government regulatory and intellectual property. Not only this, they are also recognised for their commitment to training and development.

Each year they take on 60 trainee solicitors, composed of law and non-law graduates. The two-year training contract is split into four six-month periods of work experience known as 'seats'. Trainee solicitors move around four different practice areas during their two years at Hogan Lovells – gaining a range of experiences and spending time in either corporate or finance, as well as litigation. During the second year of the contract, the firm also offers options for secondment at their international offices and in-house with clients.

In addition to opportunities for trainee solicitors, Hogan Lovells make up to 85 vacation scheme places available for students. These are split between their highly regarded spring, summer and winter vacation schemes. With Hogan Lovells, vacation scheme students have the chance to work alongside partners, associates and trainees for up to three weeks – gaining insight into key practice areas such as corporate, finance and litigation. On a daily basis, vacation scheme students are exposed to real projects. They learn to draft documents, carry out legal research and co-ordinate meetings. There is even the opportunity to attend court. This hands-on learning is complemented by tailored workshops, discussions and social events.

ibm.com/jobs/uk/graduate

twitter.com/IBMUKCareers  facebook.com/IBMUKcareers

youtube.com/user/IBM  linkedin.com/company/ibm/careers 

Been shopping today? IBM transformed retail with the Universal Product Code (UPC) - otherwise known as the bar code - over 40 years ago. The bar code now is a $17 billion dollar business, scanned billions of times each day.

DID YOU KNOW?

Malaria kills c800,000 people each year. In 2009 IBM launched 'SMS for Life' which enables health workers in hard-hit areas to order malaria medicine with a simple text message so they never run out of stock.

DID YOU KNOW?

IBM and innovation have always been great partners. Over the last 100 years, IBM has worked to make technology faster, more effective and more accessible. Today, they're focused on how they can make the planet a better place to work and live, by creating systems that improve people's lives.

Systems that can make energy grids more effective, improve water management, make healthcare more affordable and transform the global supply chain.

IBM employ talented, smart people in almost every area, in just about every country, so no matter where their talents and aspirations lie, it's not hard to find like-minded people who share their interests. At IBM graduates will gain knowledge and experience like nowhere else.

They'll also be challenged and supported to achieve everything they want in their career. And they'll find everything they need to build the kind of career they want. But it's up to them how it goes. They'll be the one in charge, putting forward their ideas, taking on responsibilities and making choices about how they get the job done.

To make sure graduates get exactly the help and skills they need, IBM provide targeted training that includes a range of opportunities – from a formal mentoring programme and tailored skills and career development to peer support and professional development through monthly forums and the IBM volunteering programme.

So it's no wonder that they've been voted 'Graduate Employer of Choice for IT' at The Times Graduate Recruitment Awards time and time again. Quite an achievement – but nothing compared to the great things their people go on to accomplish.

GRADUATE VACANCIES IN 2014

CONSULTING

IT

SALES

NUMBER OF VACANCIES

300+ graduate jobs

LOCATIONS OF VACANCIES

STARTING SALARY FOR 2014

£30,000+

UNIVERSITY VISITS IN 2013-14

ASTON, BATH, BIRMINGHAM, BRISTOL, CAMBRIDGE, CARDIFF, DURHAM, EDINBURGH, EXETER, GLASGOW, IMPERIAL COLLEGE LONDON, KING'S COLLEGE LONDON, LANCASTER, LEEDS, LIVERPOOL, LONDON SCHOOL OF ECONOMICS, LOUGHBOROUGH, MANCHESTER, NEWCASTLE, NOTTINGHAM, OXFORD, SHEFFIELD, SOUTHAMPTON, UNIVERSITY COLLEGE LONDON, WARWICK, YORK

Please check with your university careers service for full details of local events.

MINIMUM ENTRY REQUIREMENTS

2.1 Degree

APPLICATION DEADLINE

Year-round recruitment

Early application advised.

FURTHER INFORMATION

www.Top100GraduateEmployers.com

Register now for the latest news, events information and graduate recruitment details for Britain's leading employers.

JAGUAR

LAND
ROVER

www.jaguarlandrovercareers.com

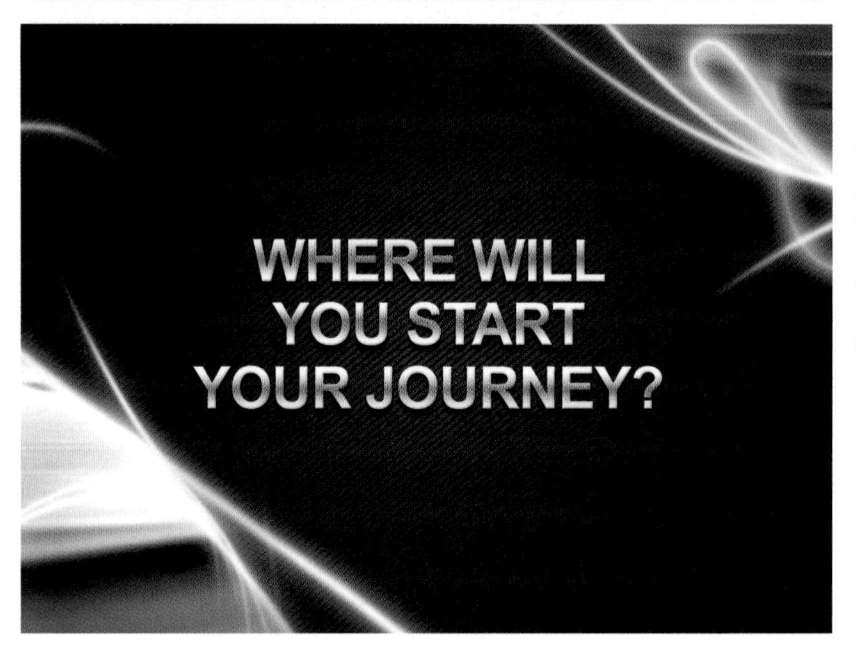
WHERE WILL
YOU START
YOUR JOURNEY?

With a proud heritage and an exciting future, Jaguar Land Rover is a great British success story. Designing, engineering, manufacturing and selling award-winning products in most countries around the world, they are iconic brands that redefine the benchmark for quality, performance and innovation.

With increasing demand and record profits that has seen the business invest significantly in new products and industry-leading facilities, their people have never been more important in the ever-evolving Jaguar Land Rover journey.

And it's not just in Product Development Engineering or Manufacturing Engineering where the opportunities lie. It's a complete business and so extensive graduate programmes exist in everything from Design, Purchasing and Finance, to Human Resources, Marketing, Sales & Service and IT.

Whichever role graduates make their own, they'll discover a dedication to excellence runs throughout the business. They'll find a requirement for innovative and creative thinking that pushes the boundaries of their potential, and ensures they develop a rigorous and commercially-focused approach to their work. With ongoing support to gain further professional qualifications and accreditation, in-house training and a thorough induction programme, the graduate scheme has been designed to be as inspiring as the next-generation vehicles that graduates will help produce.

As would be expected from two of the world's most revered brands, an outstanding range of rewards and benefits await those who have the initiative, vision and drive to contribute to the organisation's global success – including a competitive salary, joining bonus, pension scheme and discounted car purchase scheme. All this and more makes Jaguar Land Rover an excellent place to start the journey to building a genuinely world-class career.

GRADUATE VACANCIES IN 2014

- ACCOUNTANCY
- ENGINEERING
- FINANCE
- HUMAN RESOURCES
- IT
- LOGISTICS
- MARKETING
- PROPERTY
- PURCHASING
- RESEARCH & DEVELOPMENT
- RETAILING

NUMBER OF VACANCIES
250 graduate jobs

LOCATIONS OF VACANCIES

STARTING SALARY FOR 2014
£29,000
Plus a £2,000 joining payment.

UNIVERSITY VISITS IN 2013-14
ASTON, BATH, BELFAST, BIRMINGHAM, BRISTOL, BRUNEL, CAMBRIDGE, CARDIFF, TRINITY COLLEGE DUBLIN, UNIVERSITY COLLEGE LONDON, DURHAM, EDINBURGH, EXETER, IMPERIAL COLLEGE LONDON, KING'S COLLEGE LONDON, LANCASTER, LEEDS, LIVERPOOL, LONDON SCHOOL OF ECONOMICS, LOUGHBOROUGH, MANCHESTER, NOTTINGHAM, OXFORD, SHEFFIELD, SOUTHAMPTON, ST ANDREWS, STRATHCLYDE, UNIVERSITY COLLEGE LONDON, WARWICK
Please check with your university careers service for full details of local events.

MINIMUM ENTRY REQUIREMENTS
2.2 Degree
Relevant degree required for some roles.

APPLICATION DEADLINE
31st December 2013

FURTHER INFORMATION
www.Top100GraduateEmployers.com
Register now for the latest news, events information and graduate recruitment details for Britain's leading employers.

John Lewis Partnership

www.jlpjobs.com/graduates

careers@johnlewis.co.uk & recruitment_waitrose@waitrose.co.uk

The John Lewis Partnership is one of the UK's largest retailers incorporating John Lewis Department Stores and Waitrose Supermarkets. Standing out in a competitive marketplace, they pride themselves on their unique approach – by combining integrity with the outstanding service that their customers trust.

The John Lewis Partnership has evolved a distinct brand of retailing that customers recognise and trust. Alongside this, they've grown to become experts in training, developing and nurturing graduates into some of the industry's most successful professionals and managers. Whilst John Lewis and Waitrose share principles of quality, service and value, they are distinct businesses working in different but equally challenging industry sectors.

The Partnership offers a range of exciting graduate schemes for ambitious individuals seeking early challenge and responsibility. The schemes include retail management for store-based managers of the future; head office roles, perfect for those who'd prefer to develop specialist expertise in key business support functions, and an ambitious general management programme with insights into a range of business activities for those demonstrating exceptional leadership potential.

Because everyone who works for the John Lewis Partnership co-owns it as a Partner, graduates will find the opportunity to shape the way the business is run, share in its profits, and benefit from a host of exceptional benefits.

The John Lewis Partnership is looking for graduates who are ambitious, eager to learn, ready for a challenge, the kind of person who wants to get stuck in to the day to day running of a business as well as contribute to the long term strategic vision through real responsibility and challenges. Visit the website for more inspiration.

GRADUATE VACANCIES IN 2014

- FINANCE
- GENERAL MANAGEMENT
- IT
- PURCHASING
- RETAILING

NUMBER OF VACANCIES

65 graduate jobs

LOCATIONS OF VACANCIES

STARTING SALARY FOR 2014

£26,000-£29,000

Dependent on scheme – please see website for full details.

UNIVERSITY VISITS IN 2013-14

ASTON, BATH, BIRMINGHAM, BRISTOL, BRUNEL, CAMBRIDGE, CARDIFF, DURHAM, EDINBURGH, EXETER, LEEDS, LEICESTER, LIVERPOOL, LOUGHBOROUGH, MANCHESTER, NEWCASTLE, NORTHUMBRIA, NOTTINGHAM, NOTTINGHAM TRENT, OXFORD, READING, SHEFFIELD, SOUTHAMPTON, WARWICK

Please check with your university careers service for full details of local events.

MINIMUM ENTRY REQUIREMENTS

Dependent on scheme

Please see website for full details.

APPLICATION DEADLINE

1st December 2013

FURTHER INFORMATION

www.Top100GraduateEmployers.com

Register now for the latest news, events information and graduate recruitment details for Britain's leading employers.

www.kpmg.co.uk/times100

facebook.com/KPMGRecruitment   uk-fmgraduates@kpmg.co.uk 

linkedin.com/company/kpmg twitter.com/kpmgrecruitment

KPMG is a global network of professional firms providing Audit, Tax and Consultancy services to some of the world's biggest businesses. In the UK alone, KPMG has 22 offices and over 10,000 partners and staff. It has a diverse range of graduate programmes offering various professional qualifications.

KPMG believes in keeping its promises. It's what their business is built on. After all, when some of the world's biggest companies hand over their audit, tax or consulting challenges to KPMG, they need to know there's no margin for error.

Of course, the way to keep promises is to be clear about what will be delivered. So, for graduates, they offer exceptional training for professional qualifications (with an enviable pass rate few can match), tons of exposure and 'real world, real time' responsibility. But their graduates have to work for it – and certainly aren't running the show from day one. The fact is, they are grateful for that. It's a complex business, and it takes time – no matter how smart a graduate is – before they can really get their heads around it.

Of course, that's what also makes it such a stimulating place to be. For those who thrive on intellectual challenge, problem solving, working out the big picture through processing the details – and still having to think on their feet – it could be just the right place for them.

There's no one type of person that succeeds at KPMG though. It's a massively diverse business. There's room for all kinds of skills, qualities and experiences. Their clients operate in a huge range of business sectors – and to give those clients the best service means providing them with experts who really understand them, whether that's an auditor, management consultant, tax specialist or technologist. As KPMG sees it, their people are absolutely at the heart of their continued success.

GRADUATE VACANCIES IN 2014

ACCOUNTANCY
CONSULTING
FINANCE
HUMAN RESOURCES
IT

NUMBER OF VACANCIES

800+ graduate jobs

LOCATIONS OF VACANCIES

STARTING SALARY FOR 2014

£Competitive

UNIVERSITY VISITS IN 2013-14

ASTON, BATH, BIRMINGHAM, BRISTOL, CAMBRIDGE, CARDIFF, CITY, DURHAM, EDINBURGH, EXETER, GLASGOW, HERIOT WATT, IMPERIAL COLLEGE LONDON, KING'S COLLEGE LONDON, LANCASTER, LEEDS, LEICESTER, LIVERPOOL, LONDON SCHOOL OF ECONOMICS, LOUGHBOROUGH, MANCHESTER, NEWCASTLE, NORTHUMBRIA, NOTTINGHAM, OXFORD, QUEEN MARY LONDON, ROYAL HOLLOWAY LONDON, SCHOOL OF AFRICAN STUDIES, SHEFFIELD, SOUTHAMPTON, ST ANDREWS, STRATHCLYDE, UNIVERSITY COLLEGE LONDON, WARWICK, YORK

Please check with your university careers service for full details of local events.

MINIMUM ENTRY REQUIREMENTS

2.1 Degree

320 UCAS points

APPLICATION DEADLINE

Year-round recruitment

FURTHER INFORMATION

www.Top100GraduateEmployers.com

Register now for the latest news, events information and graduate recruitment details for Britain's leading employers.

L'ORÉAL

www.lorealbusinessclass.co.uk

twitter.com/LorealGradJobs facebook.com/LorealGradJobsUKI 

L'Oréal is the number one cosmetics group in the world. Every second, 130 of their products are sold worldwide. Their industry is relentlessly competitive, their business is equally dynamic, and the opportunities they offer are truly outstanding.

Joining L'Oréal means working on some of the most innovative and recognised brands there are. Their 27 global brands reach a billion customers, and they have ambitions of reaching a billion more. Their portfolio includes world-famous names like L'Oréal Paris, Lancôme, The Body Shop and Diesel – ranges that are loved by customers and trusted by professionals worldwide. Their graduates play an important role in this success.

L'Oréal's year-long Management Training Scheme and Industrial Placement Scheme cover four vital business areas: Commercial, Marketing, Finance, and Supply Chain. Whichever part graduates join, they'll work with some of the best people in the industry to tackle high-profile projects that really mean something to the business.

Most of the training happens on the job, although it is complemented by a schedule of formal courses. Mentors, buddies and supportive colleagues round off the development experience, which is personally tailored to each individual.

Along with the training, experience and competitive salary, there is one other key benefit – a fantastic working environment. L'Oréal's people are lively, enthusiastic and friendly, and the business provides plenty of opportunities for networking and having fun, both during and after work. For entrepreneurial and ambitious graduates who don't shy away from the big projects, there really is nowhere better to build a career.

GRADUATE VACANCIES IN 2014

- FINANCE
- LOGISTICS
- MARKETING
- SALES

NUMBER OF VACANCIES
35 graduate jobs

LOCATIONS OF VACANCIES

STARTING SALARY FOR 2014
£29,000

UNIVERSITY VISITS IN 2013-14
BATH, CAMBRIDGE, CARDIFF, LANCASTER, LOUGHBOROUGH, MANCHESTER, NOTTINGHAM, OXFORD
Please check with your university careers service for full details of local events.

MINIMUM ENTRY REQUIREMENTS
2.1 Degree
320 UCAS points

APPLICATION DEADLINE
Year-round recruitment
Early application advised.

FURTHER INFORMATION
www.Top100GraduateEmployers.com
Register now for the latest news, events information and graduate recruitment details for Britain's leading employers.

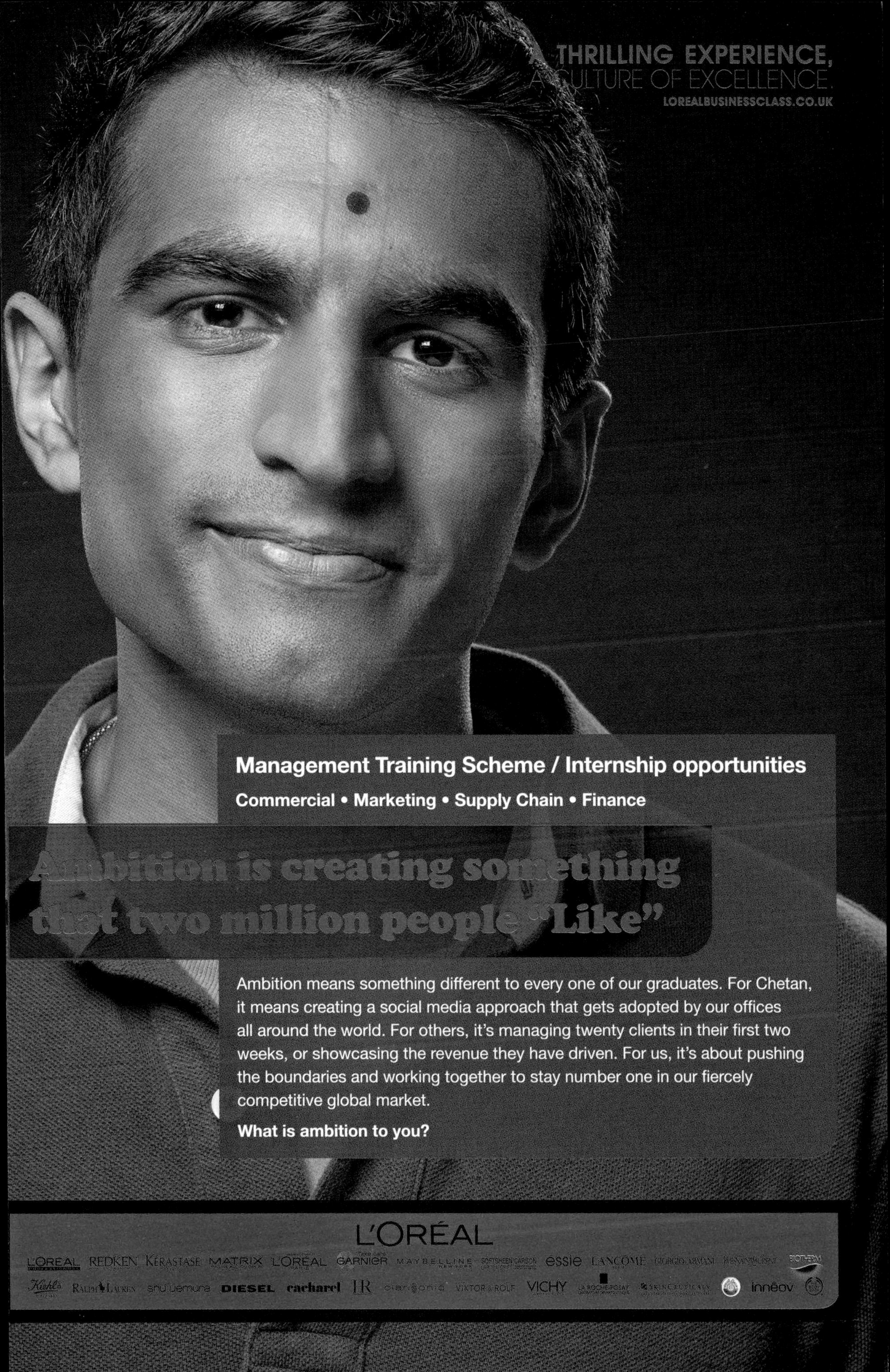
A THRILLING EXPERIENCE,
A CULTURE OF EXCELLENCE.
LOREALBUSINESSCLASS.CO.UK
Management Training Scheme / Internship opportunities
Commercial • Marketing • Supply Chain • Finance
Ambition is creating something that two million people "Like"
Ambition means something different to every one of our graduates. For Chetan, it means creating a social media approach that gets adopted by our offices all around the world. For others, it's managing twenty clients in their first two weeks, or showcasing the revenue they have driven. For us, it's about pushing the boundaries and working together to stay number one in our fiercely competitive global market.
What is ambition to you?
L'ORÉAL
L'ORÉAL REDKEN KÉRASTASE MATRIX L'ORÉAL GARNIER MAYBELLINE essie LANCÔME BIOTHERM
Kiehl's RALPH LAUREN shu uemura DIESEL cacharel HR clarisonic VIKTOR&ROLF VICHY innéov

As one of the UK's retail success stories, Lidl's simple retail philosophy and efficient working practices allow them to focus on what they do best – providing top quality products at the lowest possible prices. Their principles ensure clear structures, simple processes, flat hierarchies and short decision paths.

Lidl is an established international food retailer with more than 10,000 stores trading across Europe. With over 600 stores in the UK alone, they have an impressive schedule of new store openings planned for the next few years and are increasing their portfolio with further warehouses to support their new in-store bakeries.

Uncompromising on quality, they look for the same in their graduates. They are looking for talented, motivated and ambitious people who are excellent communicators and possess good commercial awareness. They offer graduate opportunities in positions across the UK, based in their stores, Regional Distribution Centres and Head Office. A structured and hands-on approach to training allows Lidl graduates to take on early responsibility with support being provided throughout the training by experienced colleagues.

At Lidl, initiative is encouraged with achievements being recognised; this is supported by their promise that internal candidates come first in all career opportunities. In fact, nearly all of their senior professionals started their careers in store operations and have successfully progressed in career paths through sales, property, construction, logistics and a wide range of head office positions.

With opportunities to travel internationally and an excellent rewards package, this could be one of the most exciting opportunities on the market. For graduates who have what it takes to be part of one of the fastest paced industries on the graduate market then Lidl could offer the perfect career opportunity.

GRADUATE VACANCIES IN 2014
GENERAL MANAGEMENT
PROPERTY
PURCHASING
RETAILING
SALES

NUMBER OF VACANCIES
30 graduate jobs

LOCATIONS OF VACANCIES

STARTING SALARY FOR 2014
£35,000
Rising to £55,000 after four years. Fully expensed Audi A4, private medical cover and a contributory pension.

UNIVERSITY VISITS IN 2013-14
ASTON, BATH, BIRMINGHAM, BRISTOL, CAMBRIDGE, CARDIFF, DURHAM, EDINBURGH, EXETER, GLASGOW, IMPERIAL COLLEGE LONDON, LANCASTER, LEEDS, LEICESTER, LOUGHBOROUGH, MANCHESTER, NEWCASTLE, NORTHUMBRIA, NOTTINGHAM, NOTTINGHAM TRENT, OXFORD, READING, SOUTHAMPTON, ST ANDREWS, STRATHCLYDE, SURREY, UNIVERSITY COLLEGE LONDON, WARWICK
Please check with your university careers service for full details of local events.

MINIMUM ENTRY REQUIREMENTS
2.1 Degree

APPLICATION DEADLINE
Year-round recruitment

FURTHER INFORMATION
www.Top100GraduateEmployers.com
Register now for the latest news, events information and graduate recruitment details for Britain's leading employers.

www.linklaters.com/ukgrads

graduate.recruitment@linklaters.com

twitter.com/LinklatersGrads facebook.com/linklatersgradsuk

youtube.com/user/LinklatersUKGrads linkedin.com/in/linklatersgrads

Linklaters is one of the world's most prestigious law firms – a network of exceptionally talented, highly motivated lawyers, working as a team to become the leading global law firm. Linklaters pursues this ambition by building strong, long-term relationships with clients, colleagues and local communities.

While many law firms are strong in particular areas, Linklaters is the only firm to have market-leading global teams across the full range of corporate, finance and commercial practice areas. This, partnered with a culture of innovation, teamwork and entrepreneurship, means that Linklaters is asked to advise the world's leading companies, financial institutions and governments on their most important and challenging transactions and assignments.

With 19 practices across 28 cities, Linklaters gives graduates the opportunity to connect with a diverse range of international colleagues and clients on a daily basis. As part of the training contract, trainees have secondment opportunities to the firm's international offices and to the offices of its clients.

Non-law graduates spend a conversion year at law school taking the Graduate Diploma in Law (GDL) and all graduates complete the Legal Practice Course (LPC) before starting their training contracts. The firm meets the cost and provides a maintenance grant for each. The training contract is structured around four six-month seats, designed to build knowledge, experience and contacts in a broad range of practice areas and to equip graduates for a long-term career.

Linklaters has high expectations of its trainees and recruits talented and motivated graduates. In return, they offer trainees global opportunities, world-class training and incredible rewards. Its commitment to training and development inspires its lawyers to become the best in the world.

GRADUATE VACANCIES IN 2014

LAW

NUMBER OF VACANCIES

110 graduate jobs

For training contracts starting in 2016.

LOCATIONS OF VACANCIES

STARTING SALARY FOR 2014

£39,500

Benefits include insurance, concierge service, in-house medical and gym, eligibility for bonus.

UNIVERSITY VISITS IN 2013-14

ABERDEEN, BATH, QUEEN'S UNIVERSITY BELFAST, BIRMINGHAM, BRISTOL, CAMBRIDGE, CARDIFF, DURHAM, EDINBURGH, EXETER, GLASGOW, KING'S COLLEGE LONDON, LANCASTER, LEEDS, LONDON SCHOOL OF ECONOMICS, MANCHESTER, NEWCASTLE, NOTTINGHAM, OXFORD, QUEEN MARY LONDON, SOUTHAMPTON, ST ANDREWS, TRINITY COLLEGE DUBLIN, UNIVERSITY COLLEGE DUBLIN, UNIVERSITY COLLEGE LONDON, WARWICK, YORK

Please check with your university careers service for full details of local events.

MINIMUM ENTRY REQUIREMENTS

2.1 Degree

APPLICATION DEADLINE

Varies by function

Please see website for full details.

FURTHER INFORMATION

www.Top100GraduateEmployers.com

Register now for the latest news, events information and graduate recruitment details for Britain's leading employers.

LLOYD'S

www.lloyds.com/TT100

twitter.com/LloydsofLondon  facebook.com/lloyds f

TO US, YOU'RE INVALUABLE

Visit WWW.LLOYDS.COM/TT100 to find out how you can join us.

Lloyd's is the world's specialist insurance market, insuring some of the world's most complex risks, from hurricanes to terrorism, sporting events to space travel. Based in the City of London, in the iconic Lloyd's building, it does business in more than 200 countries and territories around the world.

As well as working in the centre of the City, at the heart of the insurance industry, graduates at Lloyd's have a choice between the generalist programme and the claims programme. Lloyd's also offers an inspiring eight-week summer internship for undergraduates looking for insight before choosing their career path.

On the generalist programme, graduates choose their own placement areas to explore the many roles Lloyd's has to offer, experiencing anything from managing relationships with international regulators, to examining the potential impact of a catastrophe, to helping develop marketing campaigns.

The claims graduate programme, meanwhile, offers sharp commercial thinkers the opportunity of fast-track development towards a career as a claims adjuster in the market. Ultimately the programme is designed to develop the future heads of claims.

On each programme graduates have a series of placements, taking on live projects and real responsibility. Lloyd's makes sure everyone is confident and up to speed with everything before they start with a thorough induction and continuous training and support.

Lloyd's is looking for graduates from any discipline with good academics, sharp analytical skills and the ability to think creatively. With their impressive benefits package, intellectual challenge and real career-building opportunities in the heart of the City, Lloyd's is a superb choice.

GRADUATE VACANCIES IN 2014

FINANCE

NUMBER OF VACANCIES

25 graduate jobs

LOCATIONS OF VACANCIES

STARTING SALARY FOR 2014

£26,000

Performance dependant.

UNIVERSITY VISITS IN 2013-14

BATH, CAMBRIDGE, EXETER, KENT, LEICESTER, LONDON SCHOOL OF ECONOMICS, NOTTINGHAM, WARWICK

Please check with your university careers service for full details of local events.

MINIMUM ENTRY REQUIREMENTS

2.1 Degree

APPLICATION DEADLINE

3rd January 2014

FURTHER INFORMATION

www.Top100GraduateEmployers.com

Register now for the latest news, events information and graduate recruitment details for Britain's leading employers.

www.lloydsbankinggrouptalent.com

lloydsbankinggrouptalent@tmpw.co.uk

Lloyds Banking Group is one of the UK's leading financial institutions. With multiple brands, including Lloyds TSB, Halifax and Bank of Scotland, one third of the population has a relationship with the Group. With such a diverse portfolio of brands, it has the range of career opportunities to match.

What underpins its entire business is a vision to become the UK's best bank for customers. To do so, the Group is committed to creating better-value products and services, and strong, stable and sustainable returns.

The Group is also a place where talented individuals can fully explore their potential – and find a more rewarding career path. Because, as well as easy access to experienced senior professionals, graduates are given true autonomy to take their development to a new level. And with real responsibility from day one, there is plenty of opportunity to help shape one of the UK's largest financial organisations.

Here, graduates experience working in diverse business areas. At all times, the emphasis is on project ownership. Strong mentoring and support systems are in place, as well as formal training, and opportunities to study for externally recognised professional qualifications. Increasingly, the individuals who thrive in this environment are the ones who strive to create a positive impact through their own work, and that of others.

The Lloyds Banking Group Graduate Leadership Programme includes roles in Finance, Human Resources, IT, General Management (across a number of divisions) and Commercial Banking, which includes opportunities in Corporate Banking and working in Financial Markets. Each programme offers a unique experience – and every moment is an exciting opportunity – to make a difference with Lloyds Banking Group to help Britain prosper.

GRADUATE VACANCIES IN 2014

FINANCE
GENERAL MANAGEMENT
HUMAN RESOURCES
INVESTMENT BANKING
IT

NUMBER OF VACANCIES
Around 200 graduate jobs

LOCATIONS OF VACANCIES

STARTING SALARY FOR 2014
£28,000-£38,000

UNIVERSITY VISITS IN 2013-14
ASTON, BATH, BIRMINGHAM, BRISTOL, CAMBRIDGE, CARDIFF, DURHAM, EDINBURGH, EXETER, IMPERIAL COLLEGE LONDON, LANCASTER, LEEDS, LONDON SCHOOL OF ECONOMICS, LOUGHBOROUGH, MANCHESTER, NEWCASTLE, NOTTINGHAM, OXFORD, QUEEN MARY LONDON, SHEFFIELD, STRATHCLYDE, UNIVERSITY COLLEGE LONDON, WARWICK, YORK
Please check with your university careers service for full details of local events.

MINIMUM ENTRY REQUIREMENTS
2.1 Degree
260-320 UCAS points

APPLICATION DEADLINE
Varies by function

FURTHER INFORMATION
www.Top100GraduateEmployers.com
Register now for the latest news, events information and graduate recruitment details for Britain's leading employers.

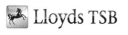

YOUR M&S

www.marksandspencergrads.com

Amazing things can happen when a graduate says "yes" to M&S. Amazing, exciting, incredible things, and that's just for starters. After all, M&S is a company with big plans – plans involving cutting-edge technology, catwalk fashion, delicious food, and growing the talents of the sharpest graduates around.

Saying "yes" to hearing what M&S can offer is where it all begins. From Retail Management through to IT, Logistics, Marketing and beyond, each M&S graduate programme comes packed with unique opportunities for bright people to achieve the best for themselves and the business.

Career progression is as impressive as the programmes are varied. For example, starting in Retail Management could lead to Commercial Manager level in as little as 12 months. Whichever part of the business a graduate joins, the end of the programme signals the start of a rewarding career with M&S – one where they'll be in an excellent position to achieve their potential as they help one of Britain's best-loved brands do the same.

The fact is, this is something of a golden age for graduates at M&S. With retail moving faster than ever before, those who join the company now will be building the M&S of the future. Whether it's spotting today's trends and turning them into tomorrow's reality, refining retail channels and enhancing shopping experiences, or developing products and services on offer, it's all for the taking at M&S.

For those with high standards, a hard work ethic and an unwavering commitment to doing the right thing, the future's waiting at M&S – along with a competitive salary and a host of other great benefits. Now all that's left to do is say "yes".

GRADUATE VACANCIES IN 2014

GENERAL MANAGEMENT
HUMAN RESOURCES
IT
LOGISTICS
MARKETING
PURCHASING
RESEARCH & DEVELOPMENT
RETAILING

NUMBER OF VACANCIES
200 graduate jobs

LOCATIONS OF VACANCIES

STARTING SALARY FOR 2014
£23,500-£28,000

UNIVERSITY VISITS IN 2013-14
ASTON, BATH, BIRMINGHAM, BRUNEL, CAMBRIDGE, CARDIFF, EAST ANGLIA, LANCASTER, LEEDS, LEICESTER, LOUGHBOROUGH, MANCHESTER, NEWCASTLE, NORTHUMBRIA, NOTTINGHAM TRENT, OXFORD, OXFORD BROOKES, READING, STRATHCLYDE, SURREY, SUSSEX
Please check with your university careers service for full details of local events.

MINIMUM ENTRY REQUIREMENTS
2.1 Degree
Relevant degree required for some roles.

APPLICATION DEADLINE
December 2013

FURTHER INFORMATION
www.Top100GraduateEmployers.com
Register now for the latest news, events information and graduate recruitment details for Britain's leading employers.

MARS

mars.co.uk/graduates

Think 'work, rest and play'. Think M&M's, Uncle Ben's, Pedigree, Whiskas and Wrigley, iconic billion-dollar brands. Think the world's third-largest food company with international operations in 370 locations. Know what makes Mars special? Think again.

Sure, Mars is one of the world's leading food companies, but it's more like a community than a corporate. Because it's still privately owned. And that means it's a place without any of the trappings of typical big business. It has a sense of humanity and a lack of vanity around leadership. It's somewhere that encourages open communication and collaboration, where people can get to grips with challenging work and take on high levels of responsibility early on.

The flat, open structure is a big plus for graduates when it comes to grabbing the opportunity to shape Mars' future. It makes for a truly creative and dynamic environment, whichever programme graduates join on. But it takes more than just freedom and responsibility to create the Mars leaders of the future. What graduates at Mars get are high levels of responsibility, a variety of possibilities and the opportunity to improve things for everyone else along the way.

Mars provides a fantastic support structure, financial sponsorship to pursue professional qualifications, extensive learning and development opportunities and personal mentoring from some of the brightest and best people in the industry. All Mars employees are called associates, and are treated as individuals, not numbers, driving their own performance and development.

In return, Mars gives its associates the autonomy to grab each and every opportunity that presents itself, and commit to improving how Mars treats its customers, communities and the planet. So that ultimately, they can make Mars mean more.

GRADUATE VACANCIES IN 2014

- ENGINEERING
- FINANCE
- GENERAL MANAGEMENT
- MARKETING
- PURCHASING
- RESEARCH & DEVELOPMENT
- SALES

NUMBER OF VACANCIES
35 graduate jobs

LOCATIONS OF VACANCIES

Vacancies also available in Europe.

STARTING SALARY FOR 2014
£28,000-£30,000
Plus a £2,000 joining bonus.

UNIVERSITY VISITS IN 2013-14
ASTON, BATH, BIRMINGHAM, BRISTOL, DURHAM, EXETER, IMPERIAL COLLEGE LONDON, LEEDS, LONDON SCHOOL OF ECONOMICS, LOUGHBOROUGH, MANCHESTER, NOTTINGHAM, NOTTINGHAM TRENT, PLYMOUTH, READING, SHEFFIELD, SOUTHAMPTON, SURREY, UNIVERSITY COLLEGE LONDON, WARWICK
Please check with your university careers service for full details of local events.

MINIMUM ENTRY REQUIREMENTS
2.1 Degree
280-300 UCAS points
Relevant degree required for some roles.

APPLICATION DEADLINE
December 2013

FURTHER INFORMATION
www.Top100GraduateEmployers.com
Register now for the latest news, events information and graduate recruitment details for Britain's leading employers.

www.mcdonalds.co.uk/people

peopleserviceshelpdesk@uk.mcd.com

Training and developing people has been at the heart of McDonald's business throughout the 39 years in the UK. Each year the company invests £43 million in developing its people and providing opportunities to the 91,000 employees to progress, whilst achieving nationally recognised qualifications.

McDonald's arrived in the UK in 1974 and currently operates 1,225 restaurants. The company has a proven track record of career progression, with the entire UK Operations executive team starting their careers on the graduate Trainee Manager programme. Prospective managers can create a long-term career with one of the world's most recognised and successful brands.

A graduate job at McDonald's is focused on restaurant management – it involves overseeing the performance and development of an average of 80 employees, and identifying ways in which to improve customer service, build sales and profitability.

Following the training period, which can last up to six months, Trainee Managers are promoted to Assistant Managers and become part of the core restaurant management team. Successful Trainee Managers can, further on in the future, progress to managing all aspects of a £multimillion business, with possible progression to area management roles or secondments in support departments. Working for a progressive company has its perks – including a host of benefits such as a quarterly bonus scheme, six weeks holiday, meal allowance, private healthcare and access to discounts at over 1,600 retailers.

Trainee Managers need to be logical thinkers, have a great attitude and be committed to delivering a great customer experience. McDonald's is looking for team leaders who are able to engage with people from all walks of life and have a passion for developing others.

GRADUATE VACANCIES IN 2014

GENERAL MANAGEMENT

NUMBER OF VACANCIES

400 graduate jobs

LOCATIONS OF VACANCIES

STARTING SALARY FOR 2014

£18,500-£21,500

UNIVERSITY VISITS IN 2013-14

EDINBURGH, EXETER, NOTTINGHAM TRENT, SHEFFIELD

Please check with your university careers service for full details of local events.

APPLICATION DEADLINE

Year-round recruitment

FURTHER INFORMATION

www.Top100GraduateEmployers.com

Register now for the latest news, events information and graduate recruitment details for Britain's leading employers.

McKinsey & Company helps world-leading clients in the public, private and third sectors to meet their biggest strategic, operational and organisational challenges. Their goal is to provide distinctive and long-lasting performance improvements – in short, it is about having an impact. Making a difference.

As a consultant in this truly global firm, graduates will have the opportunity to work with colleagues and clients from all around the world. They will come into contact with CEOs, government leaders and the foremost charitable organisations, and work together with them on their most exciting and challenging issues.

Working as part of a small team, and dedicated to one project at a time, graduates will be fully involved from the very start of their first project. No two weeks will be the same: from gathering and analysing data, to interviewing stakeholders or presenting findings to clients, the range of industries and business issues to which successful applicants have exposure will mean that they are constantly acquiring new skills and experience. Bright, motivated newcomers can expect their ideas and opinions to be encouraged and valued, right from day one.

Graduates will also enjoy world-class personal and professional development. Formal training programmes, coupled with a culture of mentoring and coaching, will provide the best possible support.

Working in consulting is challenging, but McKinsey encourages a healthy work-life balance. Successful applicants will find like-minded individuals, and a thriving range of groups, initiatives and events that bring people together.

McKinsey & Company is welcoming applications for both full time and summer internship applications.

GRADUATE VACANCIES IN 2014

CONSULTING

NUMBER OF VACANCIES

No fixed quota

LOCATIONS OF VACANCIES

STARTING SALARY FOR 2014

£Competitive

UNIVERSITY VISITS IN 2013-14

BATH, BELFAST, BRISTOL, CAMBRIDGE, EDINBURGH, IMPERIAL COLLEGE LONDON, LONDON SCHOOL OF ECONOMICS, NOTTINGHAM, OXFORD, ST ANDREWS, TRINITY COLLEGE DUBLIN, UNIVERSITY COLLEGE DUBLIN, UNIVERSITY COLLEGE LONDON, WARWICK

Please check with your university careers service for full details of local events.

MINIMUM ENTRY REQUIREMENTS

2.1 Degree

APPLICATION DEADLINE

30th October 2013

FURTHER INFORMATION

www.Top100GraduateEmployers.com

Register now for the latest news, events information and graduate recruitment details for Britain's leading employers.

The Metropolitan Police Service (MPS) is respected throughout the world as a leading authority on policing. It is their job to make London a safe place for the 8.3 million people who live there – plus the millions more who work in and visit the capital each year.

Reducing crime, and the fear of crime, in a vibrant multicultural city requires an equally diverse workforce. The MPS must continue to recruit the brightest and the best people from every background. They need the kind of individuals who can forge close relationships, build trust and understand the complex issues that affect different communities. With the full spectrum of skills, knowledge and experience they can make London safer for everybody.

With over 50,000 people, the MPS is one of the capital's largest employers. Many of these individuals work as frontline police officers with the people of London. Dealing with the day-to-day challenges of policing one of the world's largest cities is one of the most important, rewarding and absorbing roles around. In order for them to fulfil their roles, however, they rely on the support of a host of people working behind the scenes.

From Human Resources, IT to Accountancy, Forensics and Marketing and Communications, the MPS encompasses every department found in a large corporate organisation (and a few that are not). So there is a wide range of roles for graduates to choose from – all of which come with the in-depth training and support necessary to progress their careers.

Working for the Metropolitan Police Service can open doors to many different areas, such as voluntary work as a special constable (volunteer police officer). But whatever role they play, graduates can be sure of joining an organisation with unique challenges.

GRADUATE VACANCIES IN 2014

POLICING

NUMBER OF VACANCIES

To be confirmed

Please see website for full details.

LOCATIONS OF VACANCIES

STARTING SALARY FOR 2014

£Competitive

UNIVERSITY VISITS IN 2013-14

LONDON

Please check with your university careers service for full details of local events.

APPLICATION DEADLINE

Please see website for full details.

FURTHER INFORMATION

www.Top100GraduateEmployers.com

Register now for the latest news, events information and graduate recruitment details for Britain's leading employers.

SECURITY SERVICE MI5

www.mi5.gov.uk/careers

MI5 helps safeguard the UK against threats to national security including terrorism and espionage. It investigates suspect individuals and organisations to gather intelligence relating to security threats. MI5 also advises the critical national infrastructure on protective security measures, to help them reduce their vulnerability.

Graduates from a range of backgrounds join MI5 for stimulating, rewarding careers. Some join to use languages such as Russian or Mandarin, others in digital intelligence or cyber roles. Many, however, join the Intelligence Officer Development Programme, a structured programme that covers the first 3-5 years of an Intelligence Officer's career. It is not a graduate, management development or fast stream scheme. The Intelligence Officer Development Programme is designed to help joiners learn about investigations before they lead them.

New joiners are deployed into posts that offer the development of skills with direct relevance to intelligence work. These posts are outside of MI5's core investigative roles but are closely related to them. After completing two posts of one year or one posting for two years in these roles, and subject to successful completion of performance reviews and assessment, those on the programme will then be eligible to undertake Foundation Investigative Training (FIT).

The course will prepare trainees for a move into one of MI5's investigative sections, in an investigative or assessment post. On successful completion of FIT, they will also be eligible to attend an advancement interview for promotion. Following a two-year investigative posting, those on the programme will be fully trained Intelligence Officers and can then choose to remain in investigative work, or move into an operational role or corporate area such as policy or HR. They will be able to move between such areas throughout their careers.

GRADUATE VACANCIES IN 2014

GENERAL MANAGEMENT

IT

NUMBER OF VACANCIES

50+ graduate jobs

LOCATIONS OF VACANCIES

STARTING SALARY FOR 2014

£25,000-£30,000

UNIVERSITY VISITS IN 2013-14

Please check with your university careers service for full details of local events.

MINIMUM ENTRY REQUIREMENTS

Relevant degree required for some roles.

APPLICATION DEADLINE

Varies by function

FURTHER INFORMATION

www.Top100GraduateEmployers.com

Register now for the latest news, events information and graduate recruitment details for Britain's leading employers.

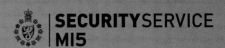

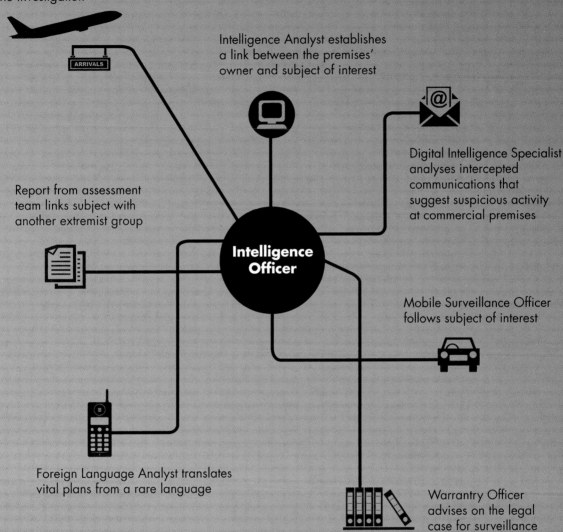

Senior Manager asks for your opinion on the future direction of the investigation

Intelligence Analyst establishes a link between the premises' owner and subject of interest

Digital Intelligence Specialist analyses intercepted communications that suggest suspicious activity at commercial premises

Report from assessment team links subject with another extremist group

Intelligence Officer

Mobile Surveillance Officer follows subject of interest

Foreign Language Analyst translates vital plans from a rare language

Warrantry Officer advises on the legal case for surveillance

www.microsoft.com/uk/graduates

facebook.com/MicrosoftUKGraduateRecruitment 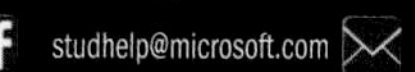 studhelp@microsoft.com

Big ideas have always been the heart and soul of Microsoft. Since launching in 1975, it's developed a portfolio of ground-breaking products and services. Today, graduates can lead the organisation into an exciting new era of technology and be a part of the world's greatest ever technology startup.

As Microsoft evolves into a devices and services company, the opportunity to stretch existing skills and build new ones is there for the taking. Thoughts, ideas and experiences are welcomed, valued and rewarded. And graduates will benefit from being part of a business that's creating new technologies that change the way the world works, lives, plays and learns.

The Microsoft Academy for College Hires (MACH) scheme provides graduates with the perfect platform to launch their career. With opportunities to work in Sales, Technical, Consulting or Project Management, graduates will work on major projects from day one. As well as learning from senior colleagues and mentors from across the business, they'll have the chance to meet peers from around the world on a number of international networking and training events.

During the 18-month MACH training programme, highlights will include: four day induction training which provides a spring-board into the business; a structured mentoring and self-learning curriculum and international formal training camps aimed at developing cross-profession skills and specialist expertise.

Microsoft also runs an award-winning one year internship scheme. With a comprehensive induction followed by in-depth on-the-job learning, bespoke skills training and one-to-one performance reviews, it's an intensive and insightful introduction to Microsoft. Interns will also be able to work in some of Microsoft's exciting business areas including Online Advertising, Bing, Xbox, Studios and more.

GRADUATE VACANCIES IN 2014

CONSULTING

IT

SALES

NUMBER OF VACANCIES

40 graduate jobs

LOCATIONS OF VACANCIES

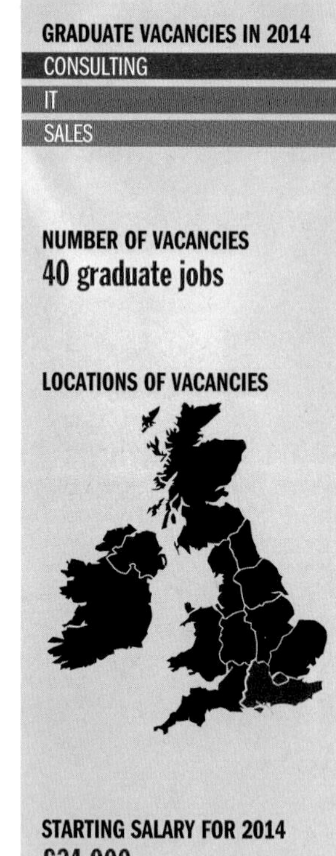

STARTING SALARY FOR 2014

£34,000

Plus a sign-on bonus.

UNIVERSITY VISITS IN 2013-14

ASTON, BATH, BIRMINGHAM, CARDIFF, EXETER, IMPERIAL COLLEGE LONDON, LOUGHBOROUGH, MANCHESTER, READING, STRATHCLYDE, SURREY, UNIVERSITY COLLEGE LONDON, WARWICK

Please check with your university careers service for full details of local events.

MINIMUM ENTRY REQUIREMENTS

2.1 Degree

APPLICATION DEADLINE

22nd November 2013

Early application advised.

FURTHER INFORMATION

www.Top100GraduateEmployers.com

Register now for the latest news, events information and graduate recruitment details for Britain's leading employers.

www.mondelezukgraduates.co.uk

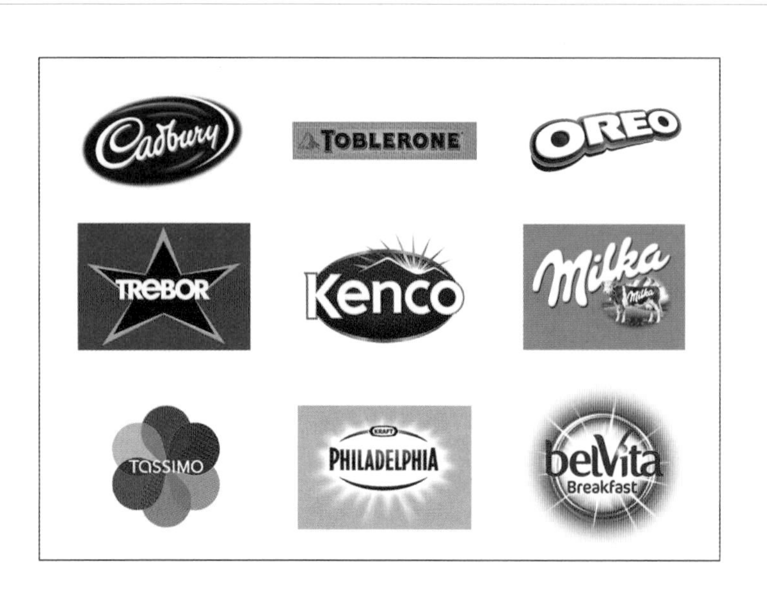

Mondelēz International is the new company behind long loved brands like Cadbury, Oreo, Kenco, Trebor and Philadelphia. With a dream to Create Delicious Moments of Joy for consumers in 165 countries, they take satisfaction in knowing that they do just that.

As well as being the world's biggest start-up company, Mondelēz International is the world's number one in biscuits, chocolate, confectionery and powdered beverages, and number two in gum and coffee. For ambitious graduates that means there is the opportunity for a career in a local market with the chance for global development.

This is far from a regular Graduate Programme though.

For starters, with just 20 graduate places, everyone who joins will be very special to Mondelēz International indeed. From day one each graduate on the programme will embark on a thrilling journey, with carefully considered placements that provide the chance to make an impact and grow. So rather than being on a designated path, everyone gets to decide where their career takes them.

Mondelēz International look for those with a head full of great ideas, coupled with the motivation and commercial spirit to apply them. In return, there will be plenty of challenges, variety and support in the form of a buddy and mentor, along with handsome rewards including a great salary and benefits, not to mention all the chocolate they can eat!

Working across a variety of brands, categories and 13 different locations throughout UK & Ireland – no two days will be the same. There will even be the chance to cast the net wider to the rest of Europe, or perhaps even the world.

GRADUATE VACANCIES IN 2014

- ENGINEERING
- FINANCE
- HUMAN RESOURCES
- LOGISTICS
- MARKETING
- RESEARCH & DEVELOPMENT
- SALES

NUMBER OF VACANCIES
Around 20 graduate jobs

LOCATIONS OF VACANCIES

Vacancies also available in Europe.

STARTING SALARY FOR 2014
£27,000-£29,500
Joining bonus and annual performance bonus.

UNIVERSITY VISITS IN 2013-14
ASTON, BATH, BIRMINGHAM, BRISTOL, CAMBRIDGE, DURHAM, IMPERIAL COLLEGE LONDON, LEEDS, MANCHESTER, NEWCASTLE, NOTTINGHAM
Please check with your university careers service for full details of local events.

MINIMUM ENTRY REQUIREMENTS
2.1 Degree

APPLICATION DEADLINE
15th November 2013

FURTHER INFORMATION
www.Top100GraduateEmployers.com
Register now for the latest news, events information and graduate recruitment details for Britain's leading employers.

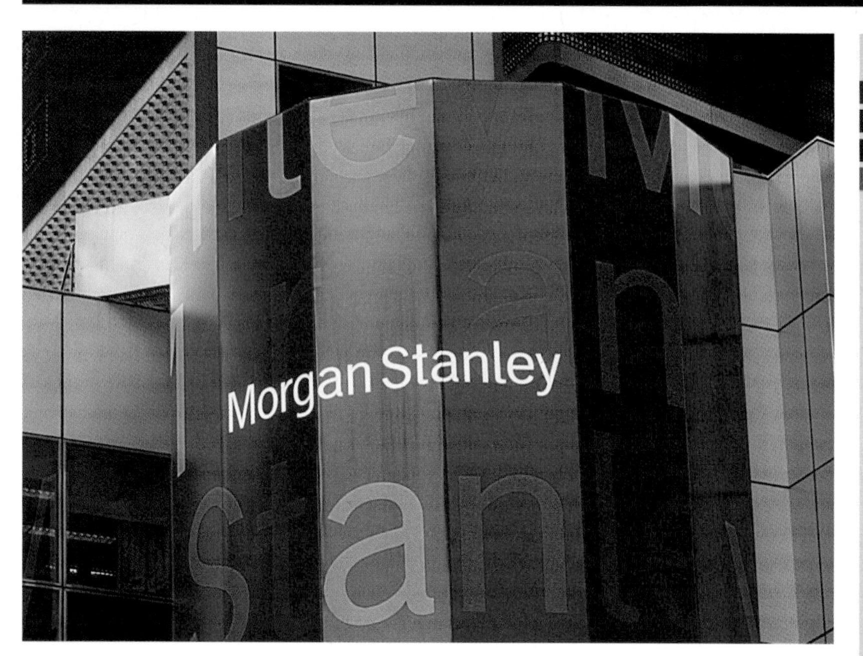

Morgan Stanley has a distinguished history of serving clients for over 75 years. Since its founding in 1935, the firm has been known for the important clients it serves, its innovative approach to solving complex problems, and its agility in embracing change.

Morgan Stanley is a firm that inspires people to be their best – and always finds new opportunities to offer them. Its mission is to build a community of talent that can deliver the finest financial thinking and products in the world.

There is no typical person at Morgan Stanley. People come from a wide variety of backgrounds and interests – all are high achievers who share integrity, intellectual curiosity and the desire to work in a collegial environment. Individuality is prized and people are encouraged to be themselves.

Morgan Stanley offers a variety of Graduate Programmes and internship opportunities for students who demonstrate the entrepreneurial drive, team working and communication skills to take the business forward. All Graduate Programmes are designed to provide graduates with the knowledge and toolkit they require to quickly become effective and successful professionals in their chosen area. Training is not limited to the first weeks or months on the job but continues throughout the graduate's career.

The summer and industrial placement programmes are considered first class and designed to attract, develop and continually assess those students who are most likely to succeed in the long-term. Through classroom-based and on-the-job training, seminars, regular mentoring, social events and the experience of working with top people in the industry throughout a period of either 10 or 48 weeks, students gain a unique insight into the industry and Morgan Stanley's culture – all necessary foundations for a truly exceptional and rewarding career.

GRADUATE VACANCIES IN 2014

- FINANCE
- HUMAN RESOURCES
- INVESTMENT BANKING
- IT

NUMBER OF VACANCIES

No fixed quota

LOCATIONS OF VACANCIES

Vacancies also available in Europe.

STARTING SALARY FOR 2014

£Competitive

Plus benefits and a discretionary bonus.

UNIVERSITY VISITS IN 2013-14

BATH, BELFAST, BRISTOL, CAMBRIDGE, CITY, DURHAM, EDINBURGH, GLASGOW, HERIOT-WATT, IMPERIAL COLLEGE LONDON, KING'S COLLEGE LONDON, LONDON SCHOOL OF ECONOMICS, LOUGHBOROUGH, NOTTINGHAM, OXFORD, ST ANDREWS, STIRLING, STRATHCLYDE, ULSTER, UNIVERSITY COLLEGE LONDON, WARWICK

Please check with your university careers service for full details of local events.

MINIMUM ENTRY REQUIREMENTS

2.1 Degree

APPLICATION DEADLINE

Varies by function

FURTHER INFORMATION

www.Top100GraduateEmployers.com

Register now for the latest news, events information and graduate recruitment details for Britain's leading employers.

www.morrisonsgraduates.com

facebook.com/Morrisons.Graduates  graduates@morrisonsplc.co.uk

Morrisons is unique. A vertically integrated retailer – they buy, they make, they move and they sell, all meaning they can offer graduates unrivalled experiences in Head Office, Food Online, Manufacturing, Logistics and Retail, giving them the best chance of reaching the top of the business.

There couldn't be a more exciting time to join Morrisons as they open more M local stores, launch food online and are expanding both Kiddicare and their own brand clothing range – Nutmeg. New format stores continue to be rolled out, where fresh produce and the craft skills of Morrisons' 'Market Street' concept become the stars of the show. This dynamic organisation has strong ambitions to become a multi-format and multi-channel retailer to be reckoned with. An integral part of that is the quest to find new and better ways to serve customers and offer them "more of what matters".

Unlike their competitors Morrisons own most of their supply chain, making them the UK's second largest fresh food producer and giving them full knowledge of the provenance of their food. As a result, Morrisons can vouch for their quality and have the shortest lead times in the business. These important points of difference mean graduates can learn fast and go far, all in a very short time.

Personal progress is actively supported and as tomorrow's managers move around, they are encouraged all the way by senior managers, mentors and 'buddies'. The key to success is a real desire to roll up sleeves and get stuck in as graduates are given lots of responsibility from very early on.

At Morrisons no-one stands on ceremony and a culture of "we're all in this together" creates an amazingly successful business – one that has recently been voted the Grocer's Employer of the Year 2013.

GRADUATE VACANCIES IN 2014

- FINANCE
- GENERAL MANAGEMENT
- HUMAN RESOURCES
- IT
- LOGISTICS
- MARKETING
- PROPERTY
- RETAILING

NUMBER OF VACANCIES
Around 100 graduate jobs

LOCATIONS OF VACANCIES

STARTING SALARY FOR 2014
£25,000

UNIVERSITY VISITS IN 2013-14
BRADFORD, DURHAM, HULL, LEEDS, LIVERPOOL, MANCHESTER, NEWCASTLE, NORTHUMBRIA, NOTTINGHAM, NOTTINGHAM TRENT, READING, SHEFFIELD, WARWICK
Please check with your university careers service for full details of local events.

MINIMUM ENTRY REQUIREMENTS
2.1 Degree
Relevant degree required for some roles.

APPLICATION DEADLINE
January 2014

FURTHER INFORMATION
www.Top100GraduateEmployers.com
Register now for the latest news, events information and graduate recruitment details for Britain's leading employers.

nationalgrid

www.nationalgridcareers.com/
Development-Opportunities

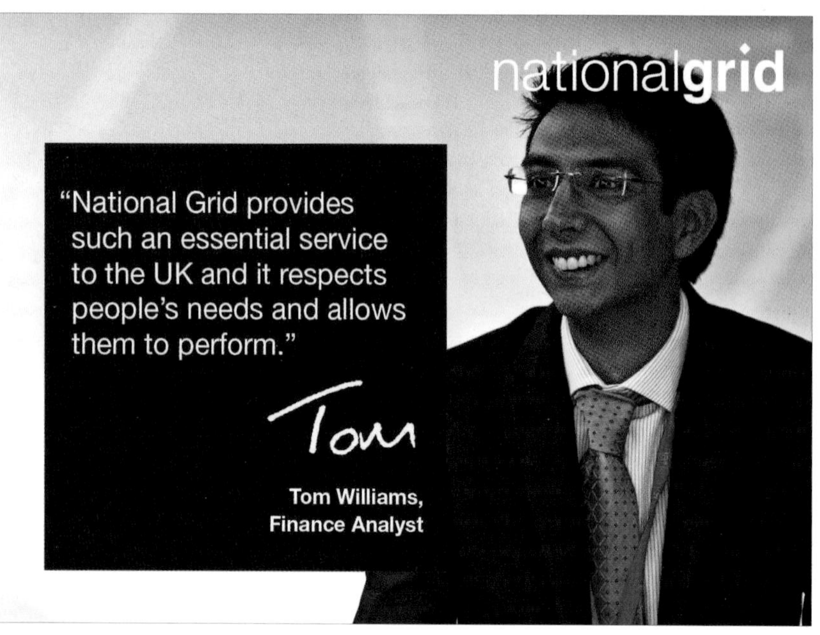

nationalgrid
"National Grid provides such an essential service to the UK and it respects people's needs and allows them to perform."
Tom
Tom Williams,
Finance Analyst

National Grid's job is to connect people to the energy they use, safely. They are at the heart of one of the greatest challenges facing society – delivering clean energy to support the world long into the future. They hold a vital position at the centre of the energy system.

National Grid joins everything up. They own and manage the grids that connect the energy sources to the people that use it. They're the largest utility in the UK, running systems that deliver gas and electricity across the entire country, connecting people to the energy they use.

Everyone relies on having energy at their fingertips: society is built on it. From the warmth and light at home, and the power which keeps factories and offices going, to the mobile communications and other technologies that are essential parts of the modern lifestyle.

National Grid is investing around £30billion over the next 8 years to develop and renew the UK's energy infrastructure, leading the way on renewable energy. There's never been a more interesting and exciting time to join National Grid.

National Grid is passionate about their "grow our own strategy" and their suite of GCSE to degree level career path development programmes. It's little wonder that they are recognised for excellence and innovation – after all, they have been running some for well over 20 years – so they are some of the best to be found.

National Grid's Graduate Development Programme offers a fantastic insight into a number of career paths, i.e. Technical Engineer, Commercial Analyst, Finance Analyst, Procurement Buyer and Information Services. It has been designed to accelerate development by offering graduates key experiences and knowledge in their relevant career paths.

GRADUATE VACANCIES IN 2014
- ACCOUNTANCY
- ENGINEERING
- FINANCE
- GENERAL MANAGEMENT
- IT
- LOGISTICS
- PURCHASING
- RESEARCH & DEVELOPMENT

NUMBER OF VACANCIES
30+ graduate jobs

LOCATIONS OF VACANCIES

STARTING SALARY FOR 2014
£25,600
£26,600 for those with a Masters.
£2,000 welcome payment.

UNIVERSITY VISITS IN 2013-14
BATH, BRISTOL, CAMBRIDGE, CARDIFF, IMPERIAL COLLEGE LONDON, LOUGHBOROUGH, MANCHESTER, NOTTINGHAM, SHEFFIELD, SOUTHAMPTON, WARWICK
Please check with your university careers service for full details of local events.

MINIMUM ENTRY REQUIREMENTS
2.2 Degree

APPLICATION DEADLINE
31st January 2014

FURTHER INFORMATION
www.Top100GraduateEmployers.com
Register now for the latest news, events information and graduate recruitment details for Britain's leading employers.

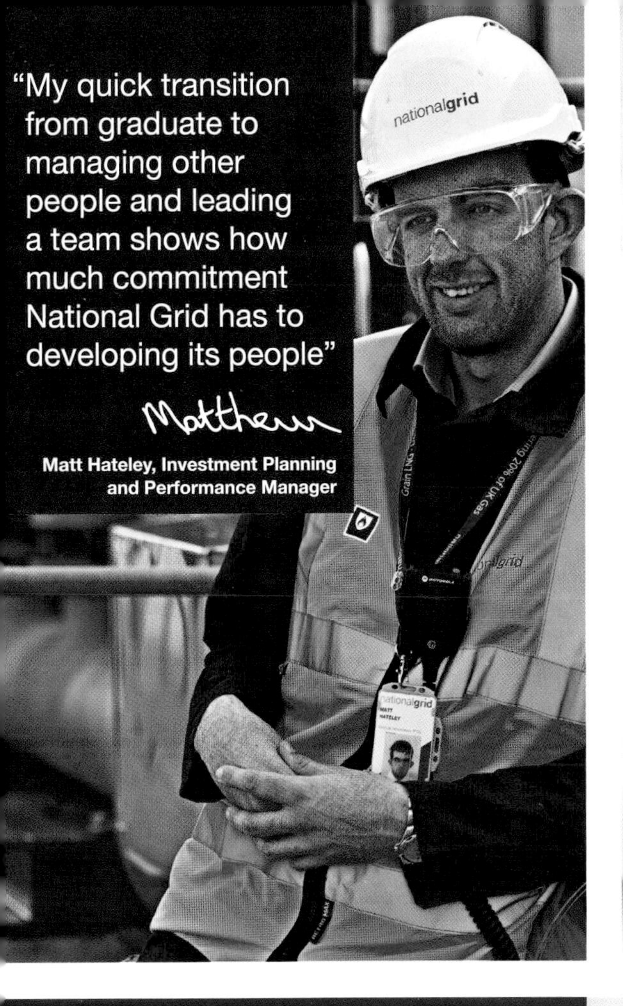
"My quick transition from graduate to managing other people and leading a team shows how much commitment National Grid has to developing its people"
Matthew
Matt Hateley, Investment Planning and Performance Manager
nationalgrid

"National Grid provides such an essential service to the UK and it respects people's needs and allows them to perform."
Tom
Tom Williams

www.nestleacademy.co.uk

nestleacademy@uk.nestle.com

twitter.com/NestleCareersUK  facebook.com/nestle.graduates 

Nestlé is the world's leading nutrition, health and wellness company, employing 330,000 people in over 150 countries, running 461 factories worldwide, generating sales in 2012 of CHF 92.2bn! Brands produced in the UK such as Kit Kat, Buxton, Felix, Nescafé and Shreddies are known worldwide.

With a presence across the world, they have a diverse, truly global environment that brings new perspectives to every challenge and opportunity. As a result, graduates will learn from exceptional people and collaborate across teams, territories and continents because this is a way of life at Nestlé.

The graduate scheme offers unparalleled opportunities to excel and develop a fulfilling career. Graduates are given the chance to contribute every day whilst making an impact long-term, growing as individuals whilst supporting a wider team. Nothing stands still for long at Nestlé, least of all employees who have the vision, desire and ability to grow – as colleagues and as people.

Depending on the scheme, graduates get involved in all aspects of a product's lifecycle from launching the Kit Kat champion campaign, to developing the machinery at the new Tutbury factory, to managing the Aero Bubble promotion.

Nestlé's International Development Programme for marketing and sales takes the top graduate talent from markets around the world and moves them onto a scheme offering global opportunities to further develop their core leadership and professional capabilities through exposure to international markets.

Graduates receive a detailed development programme focusing on regular performance evaluation and feedback as they look to perfect those key leadership skills required to be successful as a leader in the business. They also receive cross-functional exposure and work on live projects to deliver real business results. What's more, graduates are in a real job from day one.

GRADUATE VACANCIES IN 2014

- ENGINEERING
- FINANCE
- HUMAN RESOURCES
- IT
- MARKETING
- SALES

NUMBER OF VACANCIES
50 graduate jobs

LOCATIONS OF VACANCIES

STARTING SALARY FOR 2014
£27,000
Plus a £2,000 welcome bonus.

UNIVERSITY VISITS IN 2013-14
ASTON, BATH, CAMBRIDGE, DURHAM, EDINBURGH, EXETER, GLASGOW, LANCASTER, LEEDS, LIVERPOOL, LOUGHBOROUGH, MANCHESTER, NEWCASTLE, NOTTINGHAM, OXFORD, SHEFFIELD, STRATHCLYDE, UNIVERSITY COLLEGE LONDON, WARWICK, YORK
Please check with your university careers service for full details of local events.

MINIMUM ENTRY REQUIREMENTS
2.1 Degree
Relevant degree required for some roles.

APPLICATION DEADLINE
29th November 2013

FURTHER INFORMATION
www.Top100GraduateEmployers.com
Register now for the latest news, events information and graduate recruitment details for Britain's leading employers.

MY WORK HELPS US WORK.
AKTHAR HUSSAIN, Electrical Engineering
"The work is dynamic and different, with the chance to create a legacy that will be around forever."

It's natural to associate Network Rail with 'trains and engineering'. In reality, they provide the entire infrastructure and transport network that keeps the country moving. Responsible for tracks, signals, tunnels, bridges, viaducts, level crossings and stations, they touch millions of lives across Britain, every day.

Passenger satisfaction levels are high and they're experiencing record levels of passenger and freight demand. Network Rail's ambition is to continue to meet customer needs, while providing even better value for money in the future.

Investing £36.7bn on improving the network, they're delivering some of the largest engineering projects that are happening in Europe today. Their graduates are trusted to make a real and valuable contribution from day one. Whether these talented individuals are based in a front-line role or delivering critical support behind the scenes, they help the organisation deliver the railway that's so vital for Britain's economic growth.

After a period of induction, graduates gain experience on a range of placements. While there's plenty of support, it's the graduate that takes control over the pace and content of their progression. There's a vast range of programmes to choose from including: engineering, finance, general management, project management and business and information management services (BIMS).

Network Rail see graduates as the future leaders of the organisation, so they take training and development very seriously. Whichever area graduates specialise in, they work towards professional qualifications and receive regular reviews of their performance and development. They'll use their fresh thinking and innovative ideas to improve the infrastructure across the UK.

GRADUATE VACANCIES IN 2014

- ACCOUNTANCY
- ENGINEERING
- FINANCE
- GENERAL MANAGEMENT
- IT
- LOGISTICS
- PROPERTY
- PURCHASING

NUMBER OF VACANCIES
120-140 graduate jobs

LOCATIONS OF VACANCIES

STARTING SALARY FOR 2014
£26,500
Plus a welcome bonus.

UNIVERSITY VISITS IN 2013-14
ASTON, BATH, BRISTOL, CARDIFF, CITY, DURHAM, EDINBURGH, IMPERIAL COLLEGE LONDON, KING'S COLLEGE LONDON, LEEDS, LIVERPOOL, LOUGHBOROUGH, MANCHESTER, NEWCASTLE, NOTTINGHAM, OXFORD, READING, SHEFFIELD, SOUTHAMPTON, STRATHCLYDE, UNIVERSITY COLLEGE LONDON, WARWICK, YORK
Please check with your university careers service for full details of local events.

MINIMUM ENTRY REQUIREMENTS
2.1 Degree

APPLICATION DEADLINE
9th December 2013

FURTHER INFORMATION
www.Top100GraduateEmployers.com
Register now for the latest news, events information and graduate recruitment details for Britain's leading employers.

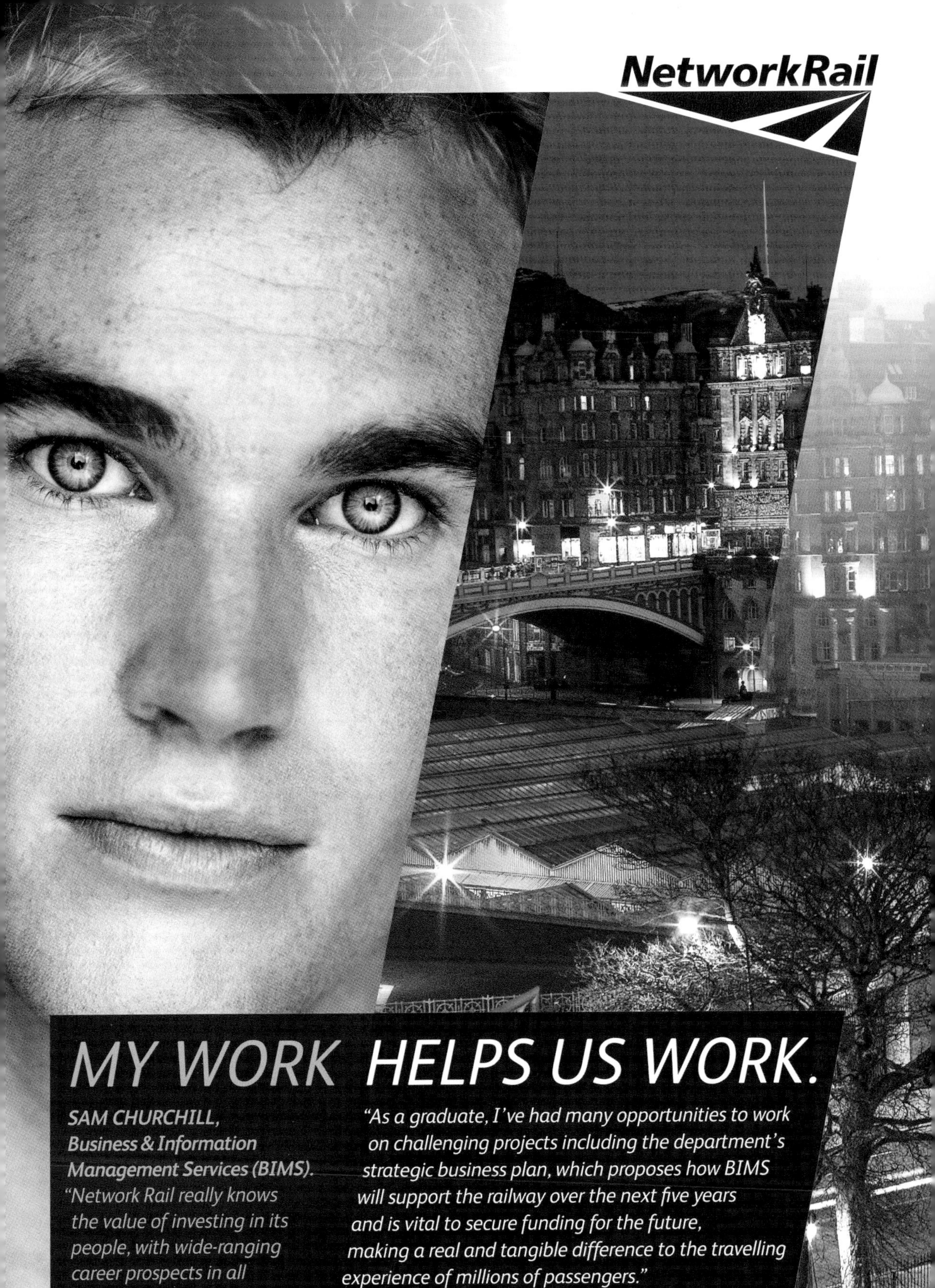
NetworkRail
MY WORK HELPS US WORK.
SAM CHURCHILL,
Business & Information
Management Services (BIMS).
"Network Rail really knows the value of investing in its people, with wide-ranging career prospects in all functions and disciplines."
"As a graduate, I've had many opportunities to work on challenging projects including the department's strategic business plan, which proposes how BIMS will support the railway over the next five years and is vital to secure funding for the future, making a real and tangible difference to the travelling experience of millions of passengers."
NETWORKRAIL.CO.UK/GRADUATES
ENGINEERING / PROJECT MANAGEMENT / GENERAL MANAGEMENT / BIMS / CONTRACTS & PROCUREMENT / FINANCE / PROPERTY / STRATEGIC PLANNING

Newton

www.newtoneurope.com

facebook.com/NewtonEurope
recruitment@newtoneurope.com
linkedin.com/company/newton-europe-limited
twitter.com/newtoncareers

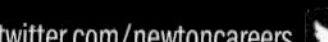

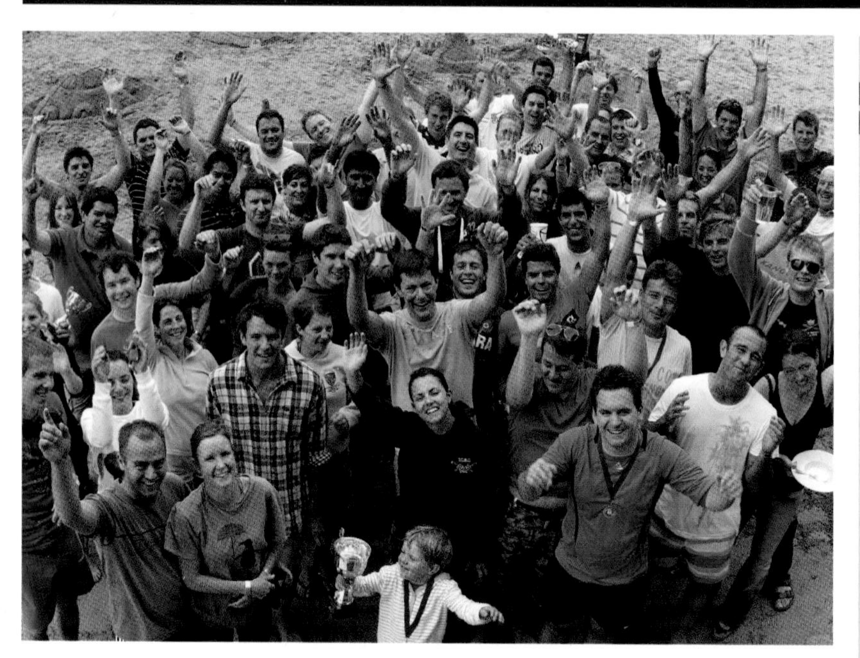

Newton works hands-on with forward thinking organisations around the world to identify and fix the cost, delivery and quality problems that inhibit operational and supply chain performance. They are looking for people that have the entrepreneurial skills and personality to grow with them.

Graduates joining Newton join an organisation with high expectations. Their clients hire them to deliver rapid improvements in operational performance and they recruit people that enjoy meeting demanding challenges and want to work in a dynamic, high reward environment.

Consultants joining Newton will be working with bright, driven people on exciting projects across multiple sectors, delivering bottom line improvements for a wide variety of clients within their first year. Newton are growing fast and are looking for people that can quickly take responsibility from the outset, and have the entrepreneurial skills and personality to progress with them.

Newton's people drive their business. It's the quality of their work, their technical capabilities and their ability to communicate with colleagues and client teams at all levels that makes Newton exceptional. This is why they've developed one of the most rigorous recruiting processes in the industry.

Newton look for people who have ambition and determination, who are confident, interesting, and enthusiastic. People with outstanding academic backgrounds, first-rate technical skills, and the ability to analyse and solve complex problems. On top of this, they need to be excellent communicators – someone who can mentor, motivate and develop the people they work with. Newton want people who are not afraid to challenge convention, who innovate and have the conviction to follow through their ideas.

GRADUATE VACANCIES IN 2014

CONSULTING

IT

NUMBER OF VACANCIES

40-50 graduate jobs

LOCATIONS OF VACANCIES

Vacancies also available in Europe.

STARTING SALARY FOR 2014

Up to £38,000

Including company car allowance and £4,000 sign on bonus

UNIVERSITY VISITS IN 2013-14

BATH, BRISTOL, CAMBRIDGE, DURHAM, IMPERIAL COLLEGE LONDON, LEEDS, OXFORD, SOUTHAMPTON, UNIVERSITY COLLEGE LONDON

Please check with your university careers service for full details of local events.

MINIMUM ENTRY REQUIREMENTS

Relevant degree required for some roles.

APPLICATION DEADLINE

Year-round recruitment

Early application advised.

FURTHER INFORMATION

www.Top100GraduateEmployers.com

Register now for the latest news, events information and graduate recruitment details for Britain's leading employers.

NATIONAL GRADUATE DEVELOPMENT PROGRAMME

ngdp

FOR LOCAL GOVERNMENT

The ngdp is a two-year graduate management development programme, run by the Local Government Association. The programme was set up to provide local government with the high-calibre managers their communities need – and to give committed graduates the training and opportunities to make a positive impact.

Local government is the largest employer in the UK, with over two million staff in over 400 local authorities and in excess of 500 different occupational areas. Since 2002 approximately 500 graduates have completed the programme, all taking advantage of the wide range of opportunities available with many now holding influential managerial and policy roles. Now is a time of huge change in the public sector and trainees will make a real contribution to bringing these changes about.

The national programme framework is built on a series of placements in key areas within a council and offers a range of experiences and challenges. All of which will provide a broad understanding of different aspects of local government in strategy, front-line service and support. Although employed by a participating authority on a two-year, fixed-term contract, graduates will also benefit from being part of a national programme group, giving them the opportunity to participate in a national induction event, join an established knowledge-sharing network and take part in an accredited series of learning and development components.

The programme has taken graduates in many different directions, with many alumni occupying key roles within the local government and the wider public sector. Ultimately, this is a chance to be part of an exciting period of opportunity and not just propose change, but be the one to make it happen.

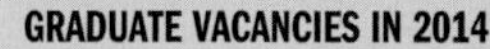

GENERAL MANAGEMENT

NUMBER OF VACANCIES
50+ graduate jobs

LOCATIONS OF VACANCIES

STARTING SALARY FOR 2014
£22,958
Plus London weighting.

UNIVERSITY VISITS IN 2013-14
Please check with your university careers service for full details of local events.

MINIMUM ENTRY REQUIREMENTS
2.1 Degree

APPLICATION DEADLINE
Please see website for full details.

FURTHER INFORMATION
www.Top100GraduateEmployers.com
Register now for the latest news, events information and graduate recruitment details for Britain's leading employers.

www.nhsgraduates.co.uk

graduatescheme@leadershipacademy.nhs.uk 

twitter.com/NHSGradscheme facebook.com/NHSGraduateScheme 

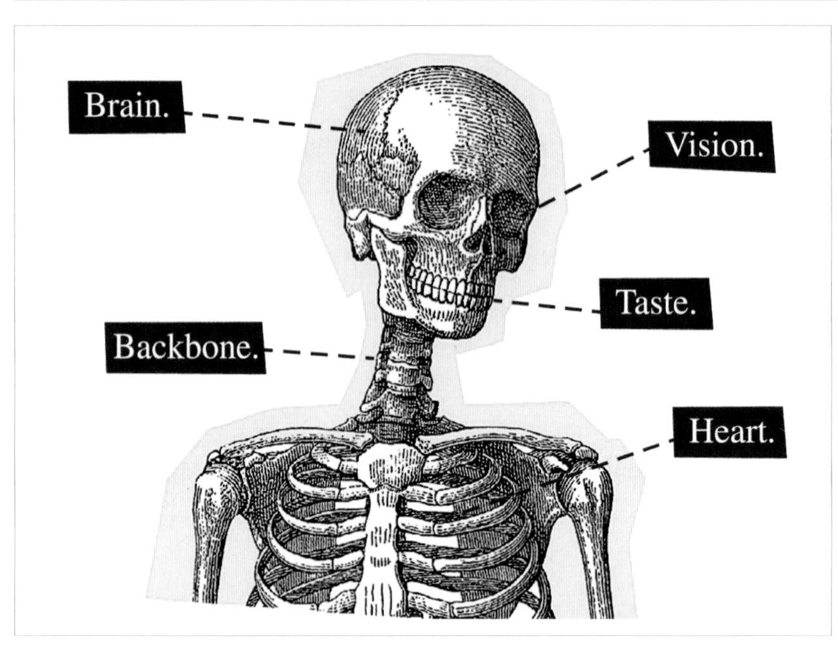

The NHS is like no other organisation on earth. Born out of the ideal that good healthcare should be available to all, it is one of the world's largest publicly funded health services. It has a budget of over £90 billion and employs more than 1 million people. This makes it the single biggest employer in Europe.

The NHS Graduate Management Training Scheme runs every year; lasting up to two years (Finance 2½ years) it has been explicitly designed to create the organisation's future leaders. It consists of four specialisms: Finance Management, General Management, Human Resources Management, and Health Informatics Management. Graduates specialise in one of these areas, acquiring relevant professional qualifications along the way.

Working for the NHS will often mean standing up to high levels of public scrutiny and having decisions closely inspected; graduates will need to be tenacious and resilient and able to respond to an ever changing environment whilst keeping patient care at the heart of what the NHS do.

The Graduate Management Training Scheme offers a fast-track route to a senior leadership role. As such, it's a uniquely demanding experience. To succeed graduates will need the confidence to tackle complex problems head on and the intelligence to contribute new ideas, but above all, the desire to make a difference to patient's lives.

In addition there is also the Healthcare Scientist Training Programme which offers excellent training opportunities within a national postgraduate training programme located in hospitals and health services throughout England. Roles are available within one of three scientific divisions: Life Sciences; Physical Sciences and Biomedical Engineering; and Physiological Sciences.

GRADUATE VACANCIES IN 2014

- FINANCE
- GENERAL MANAGEMENT
- HUMAN RESOURCES
- IT

NUMBER OF VACANCIES
Around 300 graduate jobs

LOCATIONS OF VACANCIES

STARTING SALARY FOR 2014
£22,500+

UNIVERSITY VISITS IN 2013-14
Please check with your university careers service for full details of local events.

MINIMUM ENTRY REQUIREMENTS
2.2 Degree

APPLICATION DEADLINE
Please see website for full details.

FURTHER INFORMATION
www.Top100GraduateEmployers.com
Register now for the latest news, events information and graduate recruitment details for Britain's leading employers.

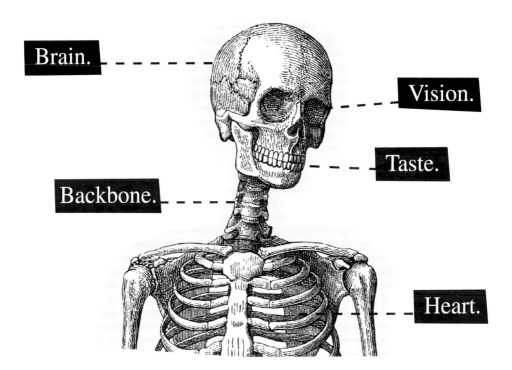

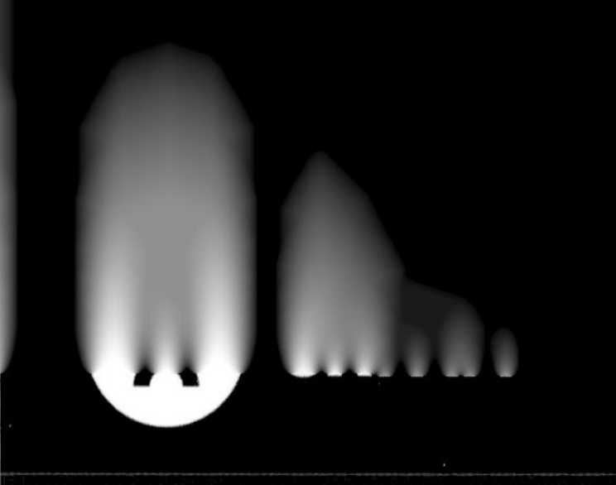

internship@oxfam.org.uk 

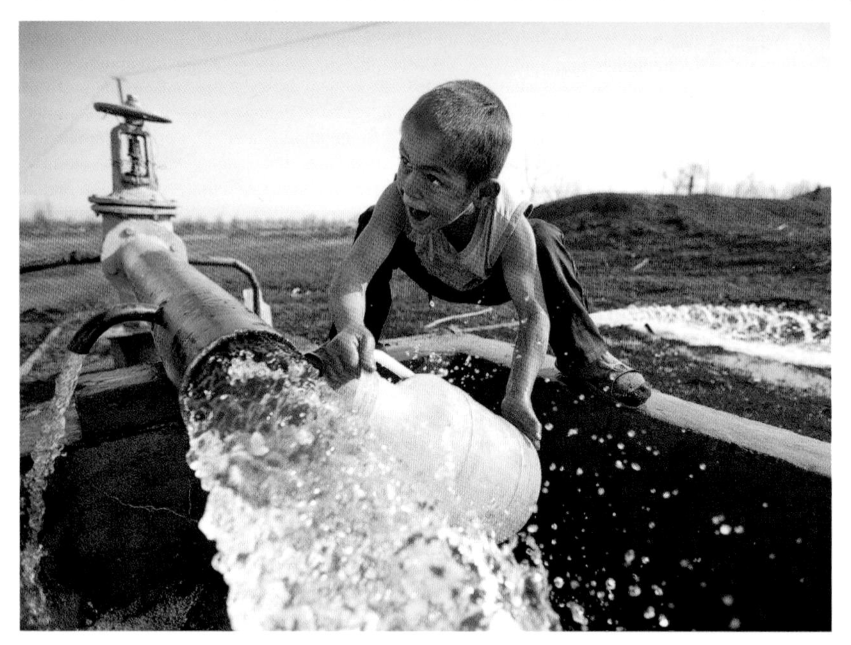

Few organisations offer such a unique opportunity to contribute towards overcoming poverty and suffering. Oxfam has been fighting it for 70 years and graduates can be part of it. Poverty isn't inevitable, so Oxfam gives people what they need to fight it.

Oxfam is one of the most experienced development agencies in the world, working in more than 70 countries. It has run its Voluntary Internship scheme since 2006 and has helped to provide valuable experience and skills to hundreds of people. Voluntary Internships provide a structured, time-bound opportunity, so that graduates can get the most out of volunteering.

Oxfam's Voluntary Internships are based on projects where its people are able to contribute and add significant value to an area of the organisation. Voluntary Internships are usually between 3 and 7 months, depending on the project. Oxfam pays local travel and lunch expenses so that its volunteers aren't out of pocket whilst volunteering.

The roles could be in Oxfam's Oxford Headquarters, a shop or a regional office. They range from Voluntary Assistant Shop Managers, to Marketing & Communications Assistants working in Oxfam's Community Fundraising team, to HR & Recruitment Advisors, to Research Executives in the Campaigns Division. Regardless of whether graduates want to plan a fundraising event, work on a campaign project, or help to run a shop, they will get to experience how a major international Non Government Organisation works and enjoy a friendly, open and passionate working environment.

Voluntary Internships are a great way to learn new skills, experience how a large NGO operates and help to contribute towards Oxfam's goal of overcoming poverty and suffering around the world.

GRADUATE VACANCIES IN 2014

- ACCOUNTANCY
- HUMAN RESOURCES
- IT
- MARKETING
- MEDIA
- RESEARCH & DEVELOPMENT
- RETAILING

NUMBER OF VACANCIES

50+ voluntary internships

LOCATIONS OF VACANCIES

STARTING SALARY FOR 2014

£Voluntary

UNIVERSITY VISITS IN 2013-14

OXFORD, OXFORD BROOKES

Please check with your university careers service for full details of local events.

APPLICATION DEADLINE

Year-round recruitment

FURTHER INFORMATION

www.Top100GraduateEmployers.com

Register now for the latest news, events information and graduate recruitment details for Britain's leading employers.

www.penguin.co.uk

facebook.com/penguinbooks

linkedin.com/company/405321?trk=tyah twitter.com/PenguinUKBooks

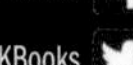

Allen Lane introduced the first Penguin paperback over 75 years ago, with the intention of bringing high-quality books to the public at a low price. Since then, what Penguin publishes has developed enormously, and Penguin has become the most recognisable brand name in publishing.

Penguin publishes some of the world's finest authors and most exciting brands, from Jamie Oliver to Moshi Monsters (with such brilliant writers as Zadie Smith, Malcom Gladwell, Roald Dahl and Marian Keyes in between, to name but a few). Penguin Group is also home to DK, Rough Guides, Puffin and Ladybird. In short, Penguin is obsessed with great content and brilliant storytelling – whatever format that comes in.

As the publishing landscape changes with developing technologies, Penguin is publishing new kinds of content, on new platforms, for new audiences. It also still publishes millions of that centuries-old, cherished artefact: the book.

Penguin has a variety of roles in areas you might expect: editorial, marketing, publicity, production, finance, operations, sales and rights but also in newer areas such as UX, Web Design, Community Management and Data Analytics.

Both Penguin and DK offer paid internships. Penguin operates a 10 week summer internship over which time each intern is placed in a specific part of the business where they will take on a particular, meaningful project – i.e. they won't be confined to the photocopier! DK internships run over 12 weeks and are placed in Editorial teams to pick up a range of creative and practical skills. Short-term work experience placements are also available all year-round.

This is the perfect opportunity for anyone looking to gain an insight into a dynamic industry with a brand that not only has a rich heritage but that constantly strives towards innovation.

GRADUATE VACANCIES IN 2014

- ACCOUNTANCY
- FINANCE
- HUMAN RESOURCES
- IT
- LAW
- LOGISTICS
- MARKETING
- MEDIA
- PURCHASING
- SALES

NUMBER OF VACANCIES
30-50 graduate jobs

LOCATIONS OF VACANCIES

STARTING SALARY FOR 2014
£22,089

UNIVERSITY VISITS IN 2013-14
Please check with your university careers service for full details of local events.

APPLICATION DEADLINE
Year-round recruitment

FURTHER INFORMATION
www.Top100GraduateEmployers.com
Register now for the latest news, events information and graduate recruitment details for Britain's leading employers.

REASONS TO BECOME A PENGUIN

1) You get to work with your favourite authors and some of the biggest brands in publishing. What could be more fun than that? **2) Our award-winning output.** Over the past year, we have won plaudits for everything from our children's books to our iPad apps. We don't like to boast, but the trophy cabinet is always pretty full. **3) Penguin is the best-loved publisher.** We have been around for over 75 years and we're still inspiring the world with stories. **4) We're a diverse bunch.** And we think publishing should be for everyone. **5) Penguin leads the digital charge.** Check out our array of apps and eBooks. Visit penguin.co.uk or follow us on Twitter. Find us on Facebook or Pinterest or read our blogs. We're always looking for new ideas and new ways of doing things. **6) People pay attention to what we do.** They just do. They can't help it. **7) We think that Penguin is a special breed of bird.** We believe Penguin matters. The books and digital products we publish enrich the lives of millions of readers around the world. They make people laugh, cry, think – and everything in between.

8) You never need to explain what your company does at parties. When you say 'I work for Penguin', everyone gets just a little bit jealous. **9) We're good and green.** Staff are entitled to three charity days every year and have their fundraising matched by Penguin. We ranked No. 7 in The Sunday Times Green List. We even have our own Penguin wood. **10) We're the only publishing company in here.** Go on, check. See?

www.uki.experiencepg.com

wecareers.im@pg.com

twitter.com/PGUK facebook.com/pgcareers

youtube.com/PGcareers  linkedin.com/company/procter-&-gamble/careers

" You lead from day one at P&G. The training is phenomenal. "
Jenna Leathers, Gillette
P&G

Over four billion times a day, P&G brands touch the lives of people around the world. They reach those who shave with a Gillette Fusion ProGlide or Venus razor, who wash their hair with Pantene or Head & Shoulders, who wear a scent from Hugo Boss, and who wash their clothes with Ariel.

The company has one of the strongest portfolios of trusted, leading quality brands, including Pampers, Ariel, Always, Pantene, Gillette, Fairy, Lenor, Iams, Oral-B, Duracell, Olay, Head & Shoulders, Wella and Braun. The P&G community consists of around 120,000 employees working in over 75 countries across the globe.

P&G attracts and recruits the finest people in the world, because they develop talents almost exclusively from within. This means graduates won't just get their first job out of university, they are being hired with the expectation that they will grow into one of P&G's future leaders. Maybe even the next CEO. New starters with P&G can expect a job with responsibility from day one and a career with a variety of challenging roles that develop and broaden their skills, together with the support of training and coaching to help them succeed.

P&G look for more than just good academic records from their applicants. They are looking for graduates who are smart and savvy, leaders who stand out from the crowd, who are able to get things done. They want to hear about achievements at work, in clubs, societies, voluntary and community activities and to see how graduates have stretched and challenged themselves and others.

Most functions within the company welcome applicants from any degree discipline. Product Supply requires an engineering degree and R&D requires an engineering or science degree.

GRADUATE VACANCIES IN 2014

- ACCOUNTANCY
- ENGINEERING
- FINANCE
- HUMAN RESOURCES
- IT
- LOGISTICS
- MARKETING
- RESEARCH & DEVELOPMENT
- SALES

NUMBER OF VACANCIES
100 graduate jobs

LOCATIONS OF VACANCIES

Vacancies also available in Europe.

STARTING SALARY FOR 2014
£29,000

UNIVERSITY VISITS IN 2013-14
ASTON, BATH, BIRMINGHAM, BRUNEL, CAMBRIDGE, DURHAM, EDINBURGH, IMPERIAL COLLEGE LONDON, LEEDS, LONDON SCHOOL OF ECONOMICS, MANCHESTER, NEWCASTLE, NORTHUMBRIA, NOTTINGHAM, OXFORD, STRATHCLYDE, TRINITY COLLEGE DUBLIN, UNIVERSITY COLLEGE DUBLIN, UNIVERSITY COLLEGE LONDON, WARWICK
Please check with your university careers service for full details of local events.

APPLICATION DEADLINE
Varies by function

FURTHER INFORMATION
www.Top100GraduateEmployers.com
Register now for the latest news, events information and graduate recruitment details for Britain's leading employers.

www.pwc.com/uk/careers

facebook.com/PwCCareersUK

youtube.com/CareersPwC  twitter.com/PwC_UK_Careers 

Opportunities are at the heart of a career with PwC. Opportunities to grow as an individual, to build lasting relationships and make an impact in a place where people, quality and value mean everything. A career at PwC means to be a part of the world's leading professional services network and enjoy the benefits that come with that.

PwC helps their clients create the value they want. From public and private companies, to governments and charities, they'll help to measure, protect and enhance the things that matter most to them.

Work directly with big name clients and get to grips with the value they're looking for by getting into the detail. PwC provides an environment to explore new opportunities and to help graduates grow while providing the best learning and development around.

No matter what year students are in at university, there are many ways they can learn more about PwC and discover where their skills, interests and career goals would best fit, on one of their work experience programmes.

PwC chooses the best people to join them, from a wide range of backgrounds and all degree subjects. As well as intellect, graduates will need to show they can build and maintain relationships, put themselves in others' shoes, and make a positive impact with their clients and each other.

For graduates looking for a rewarding career in business, the opportunity to work towards a professional qualification and unparalleled support in training and development – they'll get the best start to their career by joining PwC. They're focused on helping graduates reach their full potential while providing a competitive salary and personally tailored benefits package. It's the opportunity of a lifetime.

GRADUATE VACANCIES IN 2014

- ACCOUNTANCY
- CONSULTING
- FINANCE
- IT
- LAW

NUMBER OF VACANCIES

1,200 graduate jobs

LOCATIONS OF VACANCIES

Vacancies also available in Europe, Asia, the USA and elsewhere in the world.

STARTING SALARY FOR 2014

£Competitive

Plus a personally tailored benefits package.

UNIVERSITY VISITS IN 2013-14

ABERDEEN, ASTON, BATH, BELFAST, BIRMINGHAM, BRISTOL, BRUNEL, CAMBRIDGE, CARDIFF, DURHAM, EAST ANGLIA, EDINBURGH, EXETER, GLASGOW, HERIOT-WATT, HULL, IMPERIAL COLLEGE LONDON, KING'S COLLEGE LONDON, LANCASTER, LEEDS, LIVERPOOL, LONDON SCHOOL OF ECONOMICS, LOUGHBOROUGH, MANCHESTER, NEWCASTLE, NOTTINGHAM, OXFORD, PLYMOUTH, READING, SHEFFIELD, SOUTHAMPTON, ST ANDREWS, STRATHCLYDE, SWANSEA, UNIVERSITY COLLEGE LONDON, WARWICK, YORK

Please check with your university careers service for full details of local events.

MINIMUM ENTRY REQUIREMENTS

2.1 Degree

300 UCAS points

APPLICATION DEADLINE

Varies by function

See website for full details.

FURTHER INFORMATION

www.Top100GraduateEmployers.com

Register now for the latest news, events information and graduate recruitment details for Britain's leading employers.

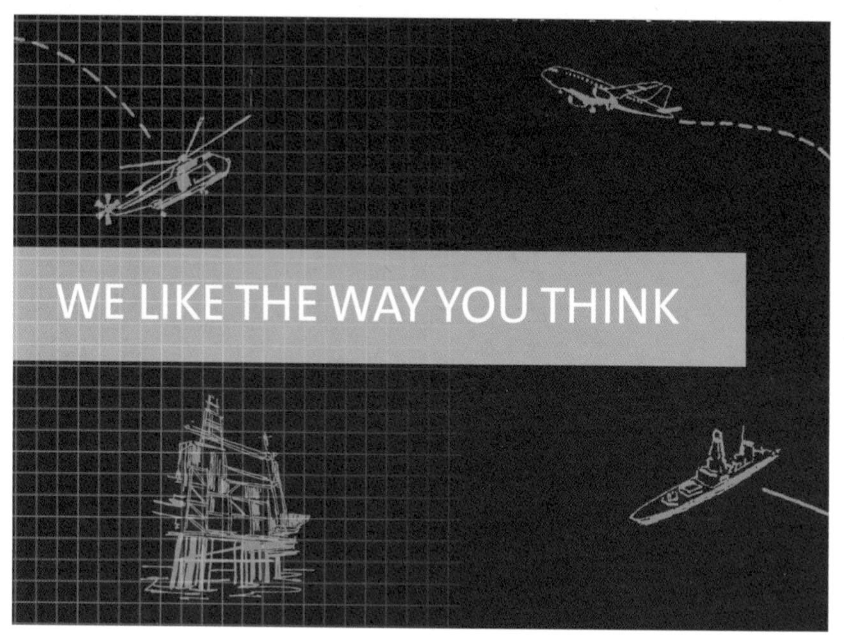

Rolls-Royce is one of the most recognised brands in the world, providing integrated power solutions for customers in the aerospace, marine and energy markets. They are the world's second largest provider of defence aero-engine products and a world leader in power for the offshore and onshore gas industry.

Their marine products are currently on 30,000 vessels and as this is being read, 400,000 people are flying in an aircraft powered by a Rolls-Royce engine. The company is a global organisation in every sense, with customers in 120 nations and an order book that currently stands at over £60 billion.

But it's the people at Rolls-Royce who power the business, delivering excellence to their customers and contributing to the continued success of the company. Which is why they look for a certain mind-set when recruiting graduates and interns. They look for people who combine both left-brain and right-brain thinking – people who can see the logical and the innovative, who can analyse as well as inspire – who love to think as well as get hands-on.

Rolls-Royce supports graduates and interns to develop their skills and gain practical experience within a world-class organisation. With opportunities spanning a vast amount of areas – from engineering to customer management – the prospects are huge. All that is needed is well-grounded talent and the ideas to make it work.

Joining one of their graduate or internship programmes could see successful applicants involved in the latest ground-breaking innovations and global initiatives. To date, they've enabled land-speed records, designed the world's most eco-friendly ships, and powered nuclear submarines. In pursuit of better power for a changing world, graduates can apply their knowledge and skills to developing the best solutions for their customers and the environment.

GRADUATE VACANCIES IN 2014

- ENGINEERING
- FINANCE
- GENERAL MANAGEMENT
- HUMAN RESOURCES
- PURCHASING
- SALES

NUMBER OF VACANCIES

Around 400 graduate jobs

LOCATIONS OF VACANCIES

Vacancies also available in Europe, Asia, the USA and elsewhere in the world.

STARTING SALARY FOR 2014

£27,500

Plus a £2,000 joining bonus.

UNIVERSITY VISITS IN 2013-14

BATH, BELFAST, BIRMINGHAM, BRISTOL, BRUNEL, CAMBRIDGE, DURHAM, EDINBURGH, EXETER, GLASGOW, HERIOT-WATT, IMPERIAL COLLEGE LONDON, LANCASTER, LEEDS, LIVERPOOL, LONDON SCHOOL OF ECONOMICS, LOUGHBOROUGH, MANCHESTER, NEWCASTLE, NOTTINGHAM, NOTTINGHAM TRENT, OXFORD, SHEFFIELD, SOUTHAMPTON, ST ANDREWS, STRATHCLYDE, UNIVERSITY COLLEGE LONDON, WARWICK

Please check with your university careers service for full details of local events.

MINIMUM ENTRY REQUIREMENTS

2.1 Degree

APPLICATION DEADLINE

Year-round recruitment

Early application advised.

FURTHER INFORMATION

www.Top100GraduateEmployers.com

Register now for the latest news, events information and graduate recruitment details for Britain's leading employers.

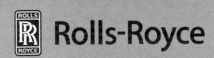

www.raf.mod.uk/careers

facebook.com/RAFCareers

youtube.com/royalairforce  twitter.com/RAFCareers

With hundreds of aircraft and more than 30,000 active personnel, the Royal Air Force (RAF) is a key part of the British Armed Forces, defending the UK and its interests, strengthening international peace and stability, as well as being a force for good in the world.

People lie at the heart of the RAF and it relies upon their professionalism, dedication and courage to achieve the RAF's vision of being 'an agile, adaptable and capable Air Force that, person for person, is second to none, and that makes a decisive air power contribution in support of the UK Defence Mission'.

The world is a changing place and so is the Royal Air Force; it is becoming a smaller, more dynamic and more flexible force able to carry out its missions. To meet the changing times and challenges, and because of the greater capability of technology, the number of people in the RAF has reduced in recent years.

However, this allows the RAF to focus on the staff they have and ensure that they get the very best equipment and training. Recruiting people of the right quality is therefore a key part of the RAF's vision for the future.

The RAF encompasses all aspects of operations, including the use of the very latest hi-tech equipment but the centre of the RAF's vision has always been its people – and it always will be. It prides itself on attracting the highest quality recruits from all sectors of society and provides first-class training and continuing development.

Officers in the Royal Air Force are expected to lead from the front, setting standards for the men and women under their command. For graduates, there are more than twenty different jobs to chose from including Air Traffic Control Officer and Logistics or Flight Operations Officer, as well as opportunities for qualified doctors, nurses and dentists.

GRADUATE VACANCIES IN 2014

- ENGINEERING
- GENERAL MANAGEMENT
- HUMAN RESOURCES
- IT
- LOGISTICS

NUMBER OF VACANCIES
No fixed quota

LOCATIONS OF VACANCIES

STARTING SALARY FOR 2014
£30,000
Salary on completion of basic training.

UNIVERSITY VISITS IN 2013-14
Please check with your university careers service for full details of local events.

MINIMUM ENTRY REQUIREMENTS
5 GCSEs, 2 A-Levels
Relevant degree required for some roles.

APPLICATION DEADLINE
Year-round recruitment
Early application is advised.

FURTHER INFORMATION
www.Top100GraduateEmployers.com
Register now for the latest news, events information and graduate recruitment details for Britain's leading employers.

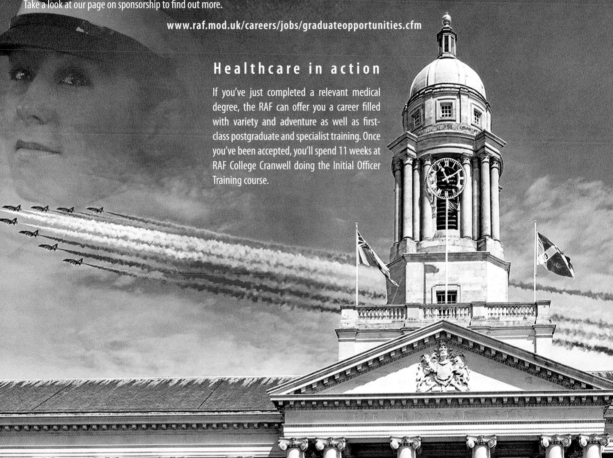

RBS Group

rbsbankyoubuild.com

facebook.com/rbsearlycareers 

youtube.com/rbsearlycareers  twitter.com/rbsearlycareers

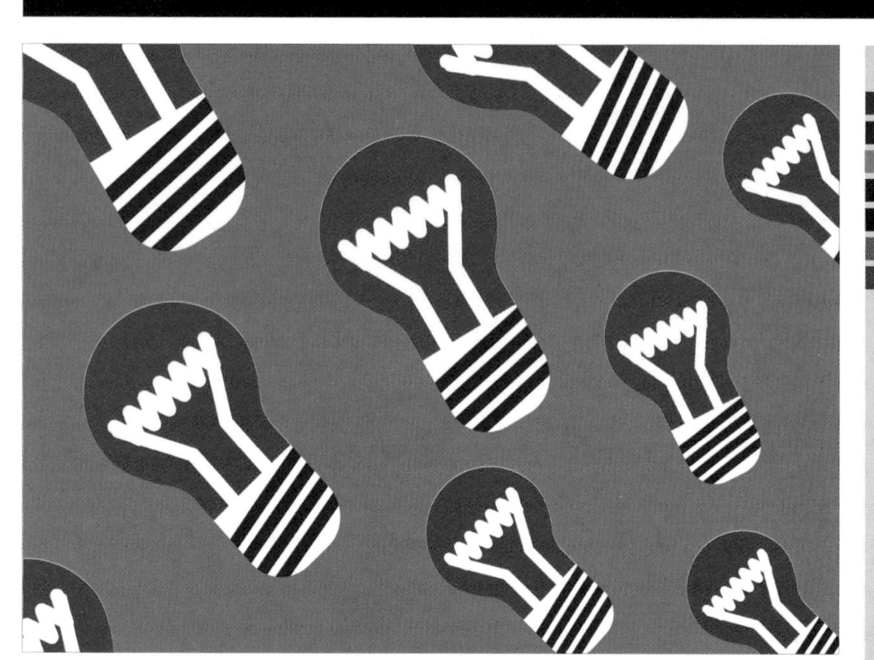

RBS is a global financial services group whose operations span the UK, Europe, the Americas and Asia Pacific. They're an organisation undergoing an unprecedented period of change, which means that graduates will have a genuine opportunity to shape the future of the Group.

RBS believes that the contributions of their graduates, interns and apprentices will build a safer and stronger bank. As a result, they look for talented individuals who can bring something new to their international business. They are therefore much more concerned with who graduates are, as opposed to what they have studied. This means that – providing that they show a passion for finance, ambition, enthusiasm and a sincere eagerness to learn – graduates from all academic disciplines are welcome.

Every aspect of RBS's graduate and internship programmes is designed to build a solid foundation to a rewarding and challenging career. If graduates have a strong academic record and the drive to succeed in a competitive and constantly changing industry, the bank will give them the tools they need to develop their existing skills and knowledge. Access to world-class training and development programmes, early responsibility and exposure to different business areas are significant factors in achieving this, as is the support of a strong network of managers and mentors. The bank also makes sure graduate talent has plenty of opportunities to build relationships through a wide range of educational, social and community initiatives.

RBS offers a variety of early careers opportunities, including technical roles in markets and banking, and specialist careers in head office functions. Each focuses on a different area of RBS's business and offers the scope for driven individuals to play their part.

GRADUATE VACANCIES IN 2014

- ACCOUNTANCY
- FINANCE
- GENERAL MANAGEMENT
- HUMAN RESOURCES
- INVESTMENT BANKING
- IT
- MARKETING

NUMBER OF VACANCIES
350+ graduate jobs

LOCATIONS OF VACANCIES

Vacancies also available in Europe, Asia, the USA and elsewhere in the world.

STARTING SALARY FOR 2014
£Competitive

UNIVERSITY VISITS IN 2013-14
BIRMINGHAM, BRISTOL, CAMBRIDGE, DURHAM, EDINBURGH, EXETER, IMPERIAL COLLEGE LONDON, LEEDS, LONDON SCHOOL OF ECONOMICS, MANCHESTER, NOTTINGHAM, OXFORD, SHEFFIELD, STRATHCLYDE, UNIVERSITY COLLEGE LONDON, WARWICK
Please check with your university careers service for full details of local events.

MINIMUM ENTRY REQUIREMENTS
2.1 Degree

APPLICATION DEADLINE
Varies by function

FURTHER INFORMATION
www.Top100GraduateEmployers.com
Register now for the latest news, events information and graduate recruitment details for Britain's leading employers.

www.royalnavy.mod.uk/careers

twitter.com/RoyalNavy  facebook.com/RoyalNavyRecruitment 

Throughout the course of history, a life at sea has always attracted those with a taste for travel and adventure. But in today's unpredictable job market, there are now plenty of other reasons for graduates and final-year students to consider a challenging and wide-ranging career with the Royal Navy.

The Royal Navy is, first and foremost, a fighting force, serving alongside Britain's allies in conflicts around the world. It also protects UK ports, fishing grounds and merchant ships, helping to combat international smuggling, terrorism and piracy. Increasingly, its 35,000 personnel are involved in humanitarian and relief missions, where their skills, discipline and resourcefulness make a real difference to people's lives.

Graduates are able to join the Royal Navy as Officers – the senior leadership and management team in the various branches, which range from Engineering and Warfare to Medical, the Fleet Air Arm and Logistics. Starting salaries of at least £24,600 rising to £29,500 in the first year compare well with those in industry.

Those wanting to join the Royal Navy as an Engineer – either Marine, Weapon or Engineer Officer, above or below the water (traditionally men only for the submarine service; women will serve on submarines for the first time by the end of 2013) – could work on anything from sensitive electronics to massive gas-turbine engines and nuclear weapons. What's more, the Royal Navy can offer a secure, flexible career with the potential to extend to age 50.

The opportunities for early responsibility, career development, sport, recreation and travel exceed any in civilian life. With its global reach and responsibilities, the Royal Navy still offers the chance to see the world, while pursuing a challenging, varied and fulfilling career.

GRADUATE VACANCIES IN 2014

- ENGINEERING
- FINANCE
- GENERAL MANAGEMENT
- HUMAN RESOURCES
- IT
- LAW
- LOGISTICS
- RESEARCH & DEVELOPMENT

NUMBER OF VACANCIES

No fixed quota

LOCATIONS OF VACANCIES

Vacancies also available elsewhere in the world.

STARTING SALARY FOR 2014

£24,600

Plus a one-off joining bonus of £27,000 (subject to specialisation – please see website for full details).

UNIVERSITY VISITS IN 2013-14

BATH, BELFAST, CARDIFF, DUNDEE, DURHAM, EDINBURGH, EXETER, HULL, IMPERIAL COLLEGE LONDON, KING'S COLLEGE LONDON, LEEDS, LIVERPOOL, LOUGHBOROUGH, NEWCASTLE, NOTTINGHAM, OXFORD, SHEFFIELD, SOUTHAMPTON, STIRLING, SURREY, ULSTER, UNIVERSITY COLLEGE LONDON, WARWICK, YORK

Please check with your university careers service for full details of local events.

MINIMUM ENTRY REQUIREMENTS

Relevant degree required for some roles.

APPLICATION DEADLINE

Year-round recruitment

FURTHER INFORMATION

www.Top100GraduateEmployers.com

Register now for the latest news, events information and graduate recruitment details for Britain's leading employers.

Sainsbury's

sainsburys.jobs/graduates

grad.recruitment@sainsburys.co.uk

Sainsbury's is a retailer with a great heritage and a clear, purposeful vision for the future. They serve more than 23 million customers a week – a market share of 16.8% – and stock over 30,000 products in more than 1,000 stores across the UK run by around 150,000 employees.

As the oldest and one of the largest food businesses in the country, they strive to deliver an ever-improving shopping experience for their customers. The numbers above prove that they have something special at Sainsbury's – a place that has become not just a great place to shop for their customers, but also a business that's a great place to work too. They are an established brand, based around trust, quality and customer loyalty that has created the perfect platform from which to explore new product ranges, enter new markets and develop their online offering.

Sainsbury's has always led the retail field. But the more they extend their brand into new areas, the stronger the bonds with their customers need to be. To achieve this, they need 2020 leaders: individuals with outstanding intellect, business acumen and ambition. Not simply graduates who want to grow with them, but natural pacesetters who expect and deserve senior responsibility very early on. Sainsbury's realise that this type of person is rare; but they offer the rewards, the challenges and the opportunities to attract them.

The Sainsbury's 2020 Leaders Programme is specifically designed to accelerate a small group of high calibre graduates through to the top of the organisation, giving them the necessary skills to influence and deliver in any business area. Graduates can join the 2020 Leaders Programme on one of the three streams; Commercial, People and Logistics & Supply Chain depending on their interests and where they see their career developing in the future.

GRADUATE VACANCIES IN 2014

- HUMAN RESOURCES
- LOGISTICS
- MARKETING
- PURCHASING
- RETAILING

NUMBER OF VACANCIES

30 graduate jobs

LOCATIONS OF VACANCIES

STARTING SALARY FOR 2014

£32,000

Plus an annual bonus based on both business and personal performance.

UNIVERSITY VISITS IN 2013-14

BATH, BIRMINGHAM, BRISTOL, CAMBRIDGE, DURHAM, LEEDS, LONDON SCHOOL OF ECONOMICS, MANCHESTER, NOTTINGHAM, OXFORD, QUEEN MARY LONDON, WARWICK

Please check with your university careers service for full details of local events.

MINIMUM ENTRY REQUIREMENTS

2.1 Degree

ABB at A-Level

Plus B in GCSE Maths and English.

APPLICATION DEADLINE

December 2013

FURTHER INFORMATION

www.Top100GraduateEmployers.com

Register now for the latest news, events information and graduate recruitment details for Britain's leading employers.

Discover

www.santanderukgraduates.com

Santander is one of the UK's leading personal financial services companies and one of the largest providers of mortgages and savings products, with some 25 million customers, an extensive branch network, over 24,000 employees and more than 1.6 million Santander Group shareholders resident in the UK.

Right now, Santander is changing the focus of the retail bank from products to customers. Another key focus is on continued IT investment and efficiency, with £490 million of planned investment over three years and continued improvements in customer service.

The company is also focused on recruiting exceptional talent into Santander UK in order to help build a strong pipeline of future leaders. Its graduate programme has been designed to provide the right candidates with a thorough and solid grounding to allow them to kick-start their career within Santander and their chosen business area. It is committed to making sure that development continues to be a much more significant part of the scheme, which is why the graduate programmes are usually offered in fields as diverse as Corporate and Commercial Banking, Finance, Global Operations, HR and Marketing, amongst others.

Because Santander gives them a high level of responsibility from day one and opportunities to get involved in essential networking, CSR and business events, its graduates receive the knowledge and experience needed to realise their full potential. As long as they demonstrate the required level of skills and behaviours, show that they're committed to making things simpler, personal and fair for customers, and have the passion and enthusiasm to succeed, Santander's people will continue to find that it is the perfect company to develop their career with.

GRADUATE VACANCIES IN 2014

- FINANCE
- GENERAL MANAGEMENT
- HUMAN RESOURCES
- RETAILING

NUMBER OF VACANCIES
50-75 graduate jobs

LOCATIONS OF VACANCIES

STARTING SALARY FOR 2014
£22,000-£26,000

UNIVERSITY VISITS IN 2013-14
BIRMINGHAM, BRADFORD, GLASGOW, LEEDS, LEICESTER, LIVERPOOL, LONDON SCHOOL OF ECONOMICS, LOUGHBOROUGH, MANCHESTER, NEWCASTLE, NOTTINGHAM, SHEFFIELD, ST ANDREWS, UNIVERSITY COLLEGE LONDON, WARWICK, YORK
Please check with your university careers service for full details of local events.

MINIMUM ENTRY REQUIREMENTS
2.1 Degree

APPLICATION DEADLINE
Year-round recruitment
Early application advised.

FURTHER INFORMATION
www.Top100GraduateEmployers.com
Register now for the latest news, events information and graduate recruitment details for Britain's leading employers.

www.shell.com/graduate

twitter.com/shell www.facebook.com/shell

www.youtube.com/user/shell  www.linkedin.com/company/shell

Shell is a global group of energy and petrochemicals companies with around 87,000 employees in more than 70 countries and territories. Shell uses advanced technologies and takes an innovative approach to help build a sustainable energy future. Its headquarters are in The Hague, the Netherlands.

With a 2012 revenue of $467 billion, Shell is the largest FTSE-100 company in the UK by market capitalisation.

Shell Upstream explores for and extracts crude oil and natural gas. Downstream refines, supplies, trades and ships crude worldwide, manufactures and markets a range of products, and produces petrochemicals for industrial customers. Projects & Technology manages the delivery of projects and drives the research and innovation to create technology solutions.

A place in the Shell Graduate Programme gives graduates real responsibilities and structured training over a period of three to five years guiding them towards a successful and professionally fulfilling career. For career opportunities there are two routes into Shell: via an assessed internship or a Shell Recruitment Day.

Shell recruits graduates within more than 25 technical and scientific disciplines, including Production Engineering, Production Technology, Geoscience and Research & Development; and a variety of commercial and corporate disciplines including Finance, HR and IT.

Prospective graduates are assessed against a competency-based methodology focusing on CAR: Capacity (intellectual, analytical and creative ability; identifying issues, absorbing information, making judgements), Achievement (enthusiasm, resilience, confidence, achieving results) and Relationships (sensitivity, influencing skills, ability to work in a diverse team).

GRADUATE VACANCIES IN 2014

- CONSULTING
- ENGINEERING
- FINANCE
- HUMAN RESOURCES
- IT
- LOGISTICS
- MARKETING
- PURCHASING
- RESEARCH & DEVELOPMENT
- RETAILING
- SALES

NUMBER OF VACANCIES
Around 130 graduate jobs

LOCATIONS OF VACANCIES

Vacancies also available in Europe, the USA, Asia and elsewhere in the world.

STARTING SALARY IN 2013
£32,500+

UNIVERSITY VISITS IN 2013-14
ABERDEEN, BATH, CAMBRIDGE, HERIOT-WATT, IMPERIAL COLLEGE LONDON, LEEDS, LONDON SCHOOL OF ECONOMICS, MANCHESTER, OXFORD, SHEFFIELD, STRATHCLYDE, WARWICK
Please check with your university careers service for full details of local events.

MINIMUM ENTRY REQUIREMENTS
Relevant degree required for some roles.

APPLICATION DEADLINE
Year-round recruitment
Early application advised.

FURTHER INFORMATION
www.Top100GraduateEmployers.com
Register now for the latest news, events information and graduate recruitment details for Britain's leading employers.

twitter.com/SiemensUKJobs graduate.recruitment.cp.gb@siemens.com

As a leading global engineering company, Siemens is behind a diverse range of technologies and services: they design and manufacture products and systems from traffic lights, wind turbines and superconducting magnets used in medical scanners, to the drives that are used in manufacturing plants.

Siemens has been finding innovative answers to some of the world's most challenging questions for 170 years. From keeping hospitals at the cutting edge of technology, to providing greener energy solutions for the way we live, work and travel – Siemens graduates are helping to provide the solutions for a sustainable future. Graduates at Siemens are encouraged to question everything and look for new ways of working.

For those looking to develop a career in Engineering, or Business, Siemens offer early responsibility, mentoring and continuous professional development. Graduates will be working for a company that's committed to innovation and facing challenges head on. Located in towns and cities all over the UK, Siemens offer a diverse range of graduate opportunities where successful applicants will be given the freedom to make their mark and use fresh ideas to keep the business at the forefront of innovative technology.

The Engineering careers on offer are as diverse as the industry itself. There are roles in Renewable & Fossil Power Generation right through to Metals and Drives Technologies. There are some great training initiatives too, helping graduates reach Chartered Engineer status.

Business graduates will help play a crucial role in helping the business run smoothly and the careers on offer include Finance, IT, Project Management and Sales.

GRADUATE VACANCIES IN 2014

- ENGINEERING
- FINANCE
- GENERAL MANAGEMENT
- IT
- PURCHASING
- SALES

NUMBER OF VACANCIES
80+ graduate jobs

LOCATIONS OF VACANCIES

STARTING SALARY FOR 2014
£Competitive

UNIVERSITY VISITS IN 2013-14
BIRMINGHAM, CAMBRIDGE, IMPERIAL COLLEGE LONDON, LOUGHBOROUGH, MANCHESTER, NEWCASTLE, NOTTINGHAM, OXFORD, SHEFFIELD, STRATHCLYDE
Please check with your university careers service for full details of local events.

MINIMUM ENTRY REQUIREMENTS
2.2 Degree

APPLICATION DEADLINE
Year-round recruitment

FURTHER INFORMATION
www.Top100GraduateEmployers.com
Register now for the latest news, events information and graduate recruitment details for Britain's leading employers.

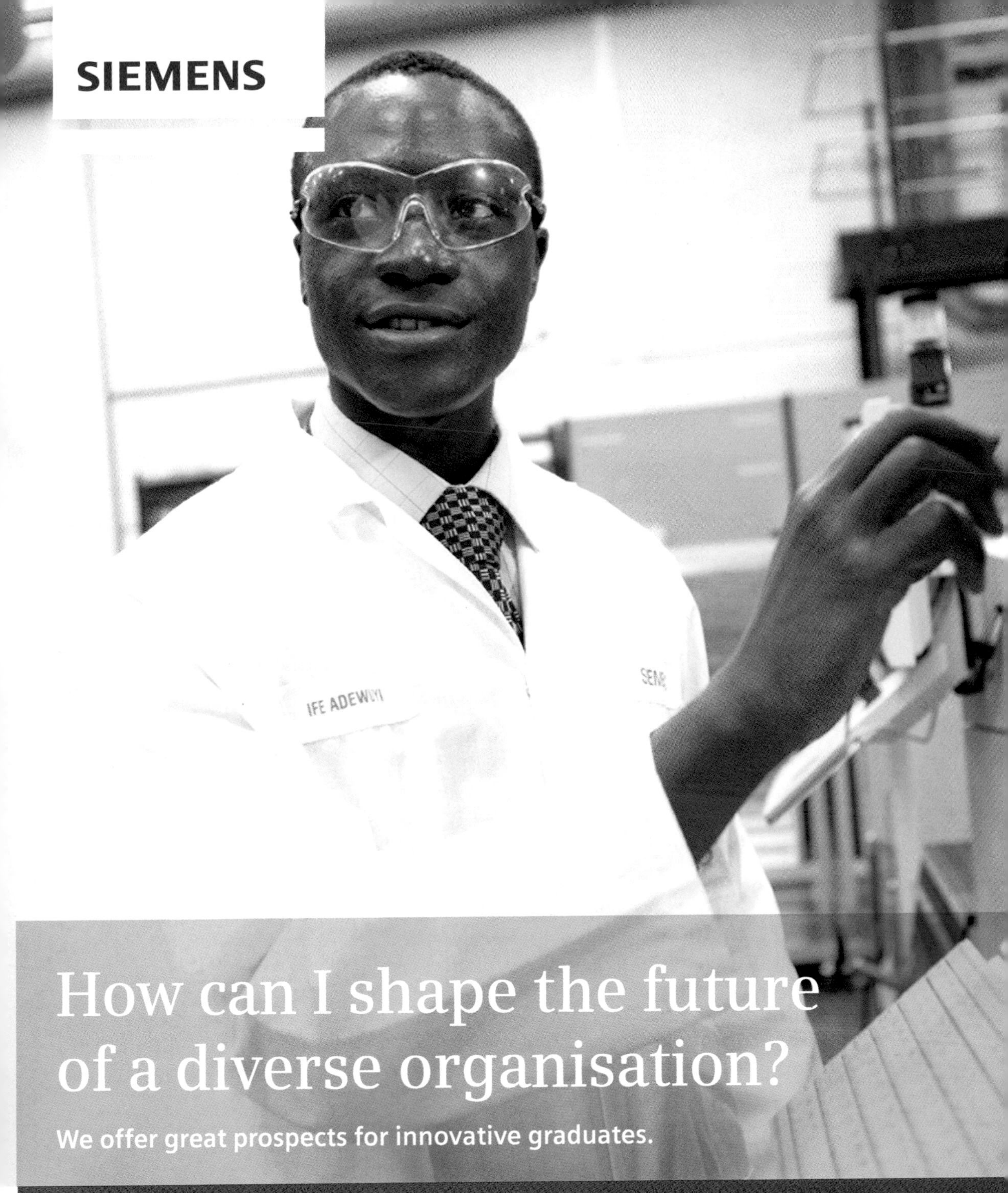
SIEMENS
How can I shape the future of a diverse organisation?
We offer great prospects for innovative graduates.
Graduate opportunities in Engineering and Business

skygraduates.com

facebook.com/skyfuturetalent 

youtube.com/workforsky twitter.com/skyfuturetalent

Sky is all about delivering spine-tingling entertainment to customers. To do this it relies on the hard work, talent and innovation of people across the business; from marketing, HR and finance to management, engineering and sales. And every graduate has their part to play too.

In an incredible industry that's always changing, Sky's experienced some rapid growth. It's launched new channels – such as Sky Movies Disney (the first time Disney has allowed a co-branded channel); received record viewing figures for Sky Sports and brought on board some incredible brand ambassadors in David Beckham and Jessica Ennis-Hill. Not to mention blazing a trail for technology development with its Sky Go Extra platform and Sky apps. But because Sky believes in better, it wants to do more. So it's looking for the most ambitious graduates with the brightest ideas, initiative and confidence to join them and make a difference.

Depending on the programme they choose to join, graduates will either be based in their state-of-the-art offices in Livingston or Corporate and Broadcasting headquarters in Osterley, West London. But no matter where they're based, every graduate has a structured and tailored plan to progress their career, as well as regular appraisals and exposure to complex projects. And with so much opportunity at Sky, there is often the chance to gain experience in a different sector, role or job function. What's more, all graduates get free Sky+HD and broadband, as well as loads of other benefits, including pension and healthcare plans, plus the ability to join the company's Sharesave scheme.

All in all, it's a compelling package for any graduate who wants a rapid start to working life as part of the next generation in eye-popping programming.

GRADUATE VACANCIES IN 2014

- ACCOUNTANCY
- ENGINEERING
- FINANCE
- GENERAL MANAGEMENT
- HUMAN RESOURCES
- IT
- MARKETING
- MEDIA

NUMBER OF VACANCIES
80+ graduate jobs

LOCATIONS OF VACANCIES

STARTING SALARY FOR 2014
£25,000-£32,000

UNIVERSITY VISITS IN 2013-14
ASTON, BRUNEL, CAMBRIDGE, DURHAM, EDINBURGH, HERIOT-WATT, IMPERIAL COLLEGE LONDON, KENT, LOUGHBOROUGH, MANCHESTER, NEWCASTLE, NOTTINGHAM, ROYAL HOLLOWAY LONDON, UNIVERSITY COLLEGE LONDON, WARWICK, YORK
Please check with your university careers service for full details of local events.

MINIMUM ENTRY REQUIREMENTS
Relevant degree required for some roles.

APPLICATION DEADLINE
Varies by function

FURTHER INFORMATION
www.Top100GraduateEmployers.com
Register now for the latest news, events information and graduate recruitment details for Britain's leading employers.

SLAUGHTER AND MAY

www.slaughterandmay.com

trainee.recruit@slaughterandmay.com

Slaughter and May is a leading international law firm whose principle areas of practice are in the fields of corporate, commercial and financing law. The firm's clients range from leading multinationals to Premier League football clubs to venture capital start-ups.

Slaughter and May have offices in London, Brussels, Hong Kong and Beijing. They also work closely with leading independent law firms around the world – these are their "Best Friend" firms. They work in seamless integrated teams with the best lawyers around the world. This flexibility enables them to work with their clients' choice of legal advisers and always select the lawyers most appropriate for the matter in hand. They constantly review their cross-border relationships to ensure that they meet their clients' needs.

They have an extensive practice providing a full range of business legal services and expertise in all key industry sectors. Their core practice areas are Mergers and Acquisitions, Corporate and Commercial, and Financing. They also have leading practitioners in specialist areas including Tax, Competition, Dispute Resolution, Real Estate, Pensions and Employment, Financial Regulation, Information Technology and Intellectual Property.

During the two-year training contract, trainee solicitors gain experience of a broad cross-section of the firm's practice by taking an active part in the work of four or five groups, sharing an office with a partner or senior associate. In addition, Slaughter and May offers an extensive training programme of lectures and seminars led by experienced practitioners, along with courses involving discussion groups that cover general and specialised legal topics. Among their lawyers, 24 nationalities and over 60 different universities are represented.

GRADUATE VACANCIES IN 2014

LAW

NUMBER OF VACANCIES

75-80 graduate jobs

For training contracts starting in 2016.

LOCATIONS OF VACANCIES

STARTING SALARY FOR 2013

£39,000

UNIVERSITY VISITS IN 2013-14

ABERDEEN, BIRMINGHAM, BRISTOL, CAMBRIDGE, DUBLIN, DURHAM, EDINBURGH, EXETER, GLASGOW, LEEDS, LONDON, MANCHESTER, NEWCASTLE, NOTTINGHAM, OXFORD, SHEFFIELD, ST ANDREWS, WARWICK, YORK

Please check with your university careers service for full details of local events.

MINIMUM ENTRY REQUIREMENTS

2.1 Degree

APPLICATION DEADLINE

See website for full details.

FURTHER INFORMATION

www.Top100GraduateEmployers.com

Register now for the latest news, events information and graduate recruitment details for Britain's leading employers.

www.teachfirst.org.uk/graduates

faq@teachfirst.org.uk

twitter.com/teachfirst  facebook.com/teachfirst

youtube.com/TeachFirstUK linkedin.com/company/teach-first 

In the UK, the link between income and success at school is stronger than almost anywhere in the developed world. Teach First is an influential charity that aims to address educational disadvantage by training and supporting people to become inspirational teachers in schools in low income communities.

Teach First believe in a vision for the future where no child's educational success is limited by their socio-economic background. Since 2002, Teach First have placed over 5,500 graduates in schools across England and Wales, and helped change the lives of thousands of young people. The Teach First journey begins with an exceptional Leadership Development Programme. This personalised programme encompasses high-quality training, supportive coaching, work experience and a PGCE qualification. The skills and experience gained can be taken forward into any career. That's why over 80 high-profile businesses from all sectors recognise Teach First's ability to effect change and develop leaders for the future. Put simply, they know that graduates who can engage, stimulate and inspire in the classroom can handle pretty much any situation in any organisation.

As well as placing inspirational teachers in the classroom, Teach First tackle educational disadvantage through their network of ambassadors – people who have completed the Leadership Development Programme and gone on to achieve influential leadership positions in education, business and beyond.

Some people join Teach First knowing they want to stay in education; some are sure that they don't; and others are uncertain about their plans. All of them find the experience of Teach First to be powerful, rewarding and enlightening. And all are changed by it.

Take up the challenge, get involved, Teach First.

GRADUATE VACANCIES IN 2014

ALL SECTORS

NUMBER OF VACANCIES

1,550 graduate jobs

LOCATIONS OF VACANCIES

STARTING SALARY FOR 2014

£Competitive

UNIVERSITY VISITS IN 2013-14

ABERYSTWYTH, ASTON, BANGOR, BATH, BELFAST, BIRMINGHAM, BRISTOL, BRUNEL, CAMBRIDGE, CARDIFF, CITY, DURHAM, EAST ANGLIA, EDINBURGH, ESSEX, EXETER, GLASGOW, HERIOT-WATT, HULL, IMPERIAL COLLEGE LONDON, KING'S COLLEGE LONDON, KENT, LANCASTER, LEEDS, LEICESTER, LIVERPOOL, LONDON SCHOOL OF ECONOMICS, LOUGHBOROUGH, MANCHESTER, NEWCASTLE, NORTHUMBRIA, NOTTINGHAM, OXFORD, OXFORD BROOKES, QUEEN MARY LONDON, READING, ROYAL HOLLOWAY LONDON, SCHOOL OF AFRICAN STUDIES, SHEFFIELD, SOUTHAMPTON, ST ANDREWS, STRATHCLYDE, SURREY, SUSSEX, SWANSEA, TRINITY COLLEGE DUBLIN, UNIVERSITY COLLEGE LONDON, WARWICK, YORK

Please check with your university careers service for full details of local events.

MINIMUM ENTRY REQUIREMENTS

2.1 Degree

300 UCAS points

APPLICATION DEADLINE

Year-round recruitment

Early application advised.

FURTHER INFORMATION

www.Top100GraduateEmployers.com

Register now for the latest news, events information and graduate recruitment details for Britain's leading employers.

Tesco's success has been built on people with the ideas and vision to shape the way the business works. People who can spot opportunities – and who will love getting stuck into all sorts of different challenges. Rise to those challenges, and Tesco will reward that contribution with unrivalled scope for development and progression.

With so many different programmes on offer, there's almost certainly going to be a role to suit graduates from all backgrounds. This is an opportunity to make some big decisions; to take responsibility for some massive projects. Tesco is looking for graduates with the skills to help the business get the best products and services from the best suppliers, and who will use their insights to deliver the things customers really want, when they want them. Of course, there'll be plenty of training along the way (possibly including a professional qualification, depending on the business area and role). But Tesco firmly believes that the most rewarding way for graduates to learn is to apply their knowledge in real-life business situations.

It's a big opportunity. And even bigger considering that Tesco has a team of over 530,000 people in 12 markets dedicated to bringing the best value, choice and service to millions of customers each week. At Tesco, even a small idea can go a long, long way.

So what does it take to succeed? Well, graduates will certainly need to be full of ambition. And they should have a good degree (in any subject). Tesco looks for people who are very community spirited and who won't be afraid to voice their opinions and ideas. Above all, Tesco wants graduates who will relish the opportunity to not only be part of one of the world's largest retailers, but to determine where it goes next.

GRADUATE VACANCIES IN 2014

- FINANCE
- GENERAL MANAGEMENT
- HUMAN RESOURCES
- IT
- LOGISTICS
- MARKETING
- PROPERTY
- PURCHASING
- RESEARCH & DEVELOPMENT
- RETAILING

NUMBER OF VACANCIES
100+ graduate jobs

LOCATIONS OF VACANCIES

STARTING SALARY FOR 2014
£Competitive

UNIVERSITY VISITS IN 2013-14
BIRMINGHAM, BRISTOL, CARDIFF, DURHAM, EXETER, KENT, LANCASTER, LEEDS, LEICESTER, LIVERPOOL, LOUGHBOROUGH, MANCHESTER, NEWCASTLE, NOTTINGHAM, NOTTINGHAM TRENT, READING, SHEFFIELD, SURREY, WARWICK, YORK
Please check with your university careers service for full details of local events.

MINIMUM ENTRY REQUIREMENTS
2.1 Degree

APPLICATION DEADLINE
31st December 2013

FURTHER INFORMATION
www.Top100GraduateEmployers.com
Register now for the latest news, events information and graduate recruitment details for Britain's leading employers.

graduateprograms@thomsonreuters.com 

More than 20 million professionals around the world rely on Thomson Reuters for the intelligent information they need to make critical decisions. The company is diverse and dynamic, serving decision makers in the fields of finance, law, tax and accounting, intellectual property, science, and media.

At Thomson Reuters, graduates have the opportunity to launch a career with a global leader. Intelligent information starts with talent. Businesses and professionals all over the globe rely on the people of Thomson Reuters to transform knowledge into action so they can shape outcomes on the world stage. The company employs approximately 60,000 people in more than 100 countries. The scope and scale of the business enables graduates to take their career in an amazing array of directions, limited only by one's own initiative, talents and goals. A career without boundaries.

The company runs Graduate Programs in Sales, Finance, Business, Journalism and Technology enabling graduates to choose their own development and build the skills they need for a successful career in their chosen specialism. With a global graduate community, alumni network, mentoring programs, volunteer days and structured training sessions, graduates have the opportunity to collaborate in their learning to develop a breadth of knowledge.

The company's summer internship program lets undergraduates gain insight into working life in the Thomson Reuters businesses. With a comprehensive weekly training plan interns are given a chance to put forward their ideas and make a real impact. It is the ultimate bridge to the graduate programs.

To be successful in the company graduates need to be smart, performance driven, collaborative and able to cope with a fast paced, ever changing environment. With so much variety a graduate will never be short of options.

GRADUATE VACANCIES IN 2014

- ACCOUNTANCY
- FINANCE
- IT
- MEDIA

NUMBER OF VACANCIES
30-50 graduate jobs

LOCATIONS OF VACANCIES

STARTING SALARY FOR 2014
£25,000+

UNIVERSITY VISITS IN 2013-14
EXETER, LEEDS, LONDON SCHOOL OF ECONOMICS
Please check with your university careers service for full details of local events.

MINIMUM ENTRY REQUIREMENTS
2.1 Degree
Relevant degree required for some roles.

APPLICATION DEADLINE
Varies by function

FURTHER INFORMATION
www.Top100GraduateEmployers.com
Register now for the latest news, events information and graduate recruitment details for Britain's leading employers.

Transport for London 

www.tfl.gov.uk/graduates

graduates@tfl.gov.uk

London
brings th
world
together
in one cit
Boris Johnson

From the famous red buses and black cabs to the Tube, Transport for London (TfL) is responsible for virtually every mode of transport in the city – and its story goes back a long way, as this year marks the 150th anniversary of the world's first underground railway service.

TfL is an innovator and its services are recognised around the world. Without TfL London would stand still.

It takes more than 27,000 staff to keep the city moving, so TfL invests as much in its people as it does in London's infrastructure. There are not many other organisations that give graduates the opportunity to see the impact their work has on the Capital. Candidates could be an engineer or quantity surveyor; go into management; have the analytical skills for transport planning or traffic control; or support the business through procurement and marketing.

TfL will give successful applicants responsibility early on, and there are many exciting projects graduates could contribute to.

TfL is in the midst of one of its greatest periods of investment. For example, work is well under way on Crossrail, a state-of-the-art underground line that will cut journey times between east and west London. TfL is introducing hundreds of New Bus for London vehicles, the greenest buses on the road, and encouraging the use of low-carbon taxis and innovative traffic management technology to cut congestion. The organisation is also continuing to improve the Tube network, including the development of major stations and lines as well as the introduction of new trains.

Whether candidates want to dig, design, plan, manage or explore corporate finance, they can expect all the personal and professional development they need. Join TfL to help shape the future of London.

GRADUATE VACANCIES IN 2014

- ACCOUNTANCY
- ENGINEERING
- FINANCE
- GENERAL MANAGEMENT
- IT
- LOGISTICS
- MARKETING
- PROPERTY
- PURCHASING

NUMBER OF VACANCIES
130 graduate jobs

LOCATIONS OF VACANCIES

STARTING SALARY FOR 2014
£26,000
Free Oyster Card covering travel on London Underground, London Overground and London Buses.

UNIVERSITY VISITS IN 2013-14
BATH, BRISTOL, CITY, EXETER, IMPERIAL COLLEGE LONDON, KING'S COLLEGE LONDON, LEEDS, LIVERPOOL, LOUGHBOROUGH, MANCHESTER, NOTTINGHAM, NOTTINGHAM TRENT, READING, SHEFFIELD, SOUTHAMPTON, UNIVERSITY COLLEGE LONDON, WARWICK
Please check with your university careers service for full details of local events.

MINIMUM ENTRY REQUIREMENTS
2.1 Degree
Relevant degree required for some roles.

APPLICATION DEADLINE
15th December 2013

FURTHER INFORMATION
www.Top100GraduateEmployers.com
Register now for the latest news, events information and graduate recruitment details for Britain's leading employers.

UBS

www.ubs.com/graduates

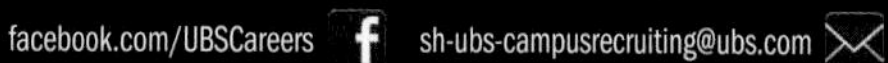

UBS is a global financial services firm offering wealth management, investment banking, asset management and, in Switzerland, retail and commercial banking. Around the world, individuals look to UBS to provide them with the advice and opportunities they need to protect and grow their wealth.

Leading companies and institutions rely on UBS's financial resources, expertise and infrastructure to help them grow their businesses, manage their risks and invest in the future. In their commitment to build the strongest relationships, provide the best advice and deliver flawless execution, UBS will not rest until they become the choice of clients – worldwide.

UBS recruits graduates from all academic backgrounds – the humanities and sciences, as well as economics and finance. Because of its global reach, the firm is particularly keen to hear from students with strong language skills. For UBS, degree subject is less important than a graduate's ability to prove they can analyse problems, plan ahead, make decisions, demonstrate sound judgement and communicate with others. The other qualities UBS seeks in graduates are ambition, integrity, a commitment to accuracy and a desire to work collaboratively with other friendly but driven professionals.

UBS's Graduate Training Program offers talented graduates continuous learning in a fast-paced but supportive environment. The program lays the foundation for a rewarding career in finance by combining intensive classroom education, coaching from more senior colleagues and on-the-job experience.

UBS is a place where graduates can expect to be stretched long after university. Whether it's acquiring the technical knowledge to create the products of the future or developing the skills to be one of UBS's leaders of tomorrow, graduates are encouraged to make the most of their talents.

GRADUATE VACANCIES IN 2014

INVESTMENT BANKING

NUMBER OF VACANCIES

100+ graduate jobs

LOCATIONS OF VACANCIES

Vacancies also available in Europe, Asia and the USA.

STARTING SALARY FOR 2014

£Competitive

UNIVERSITY VISITS IN 2013-14

BATH, BRISTOL, CAMBRIDGE, IMPERIAL COLLEGE LONDON, LONDON SCHOOL OF ECONOMICS, LOUGHBOROUGH, OXFORD, SURREY, UNIVERSITY COLLEGE LONDON, WARWICK

Please check with your university careers service for full details of local events.

MINIMUM ENTRY REQUIREMENTS

2.1 Degree

300 UCAS points

APPLICATION DEADLINE

Varies by function

FURTHER INFORMATION

www.Top100GraduateEmployers.com

Register now for the latest news, events information and graduate recruitment details for Britain's leading employers.

unilever.co.uk/careers-jobs/graduates

enquiry@unilevergraduates.com

twitter.com/unilevergradsuk  facebook.com/unilevercareers 

Unilever, a leading consumer goods company, makes some of the world's best-loved brands: Dove, Lynx, Tresemmé, Sure, Magnum and Hellmann's to name a few. 2 billion consumers use their products every day. Unilever products are sold in 190 countries and employ 173,000 people globally.

Around the world, Unilever products help people look good, feel good and get more out of life. Their impact is the result of deep thought, hard work, and carefully applied skills.

Unilever want graduates with the will to lead others in driving these brands forward. The Future Leaders Programme (UFLP) helps talent reach senior management. Quickly.

Graduates can apply to one of the following areas – Financial Management, Supply Chain Management, Customer Management (Sales), HR Management, Business & Technology Management, Research & Development and Marketing. Graduates can also apply to one of Unilever's international UFLP programmes in China, Russia or Africa. Whichever area of the business they join, graduates will make a big impact right from the start. The two to three year programme (depending on the business area) involves placements across Unilever's UK & Ireland business, alongside excellent training in leadership and business. Graduates will learn business fast. Unilever will support them in achieving Chartered status and qualifications such as CIMA, IMechE, IChemE, IEE, APICS, ICS, and CIPD. The programme is designed to give graduates all the training and experience required to be a manager in two to three years.

Unilever's challenge? To double the size of their business, while reducing their environmental impact and increase their positive social impact. Behind that ambition, and every brand, lie exciting challenges.

GRADUATE VACANCIES IN 2014

- ENGINEERING
- FINANCE
- HUMAN RESOURCES
- IT
- LOGISTICS
- MARKETING
- RESEARCH & DEVELOPMENT
- SALES

NUMBER OF VACANCIES

60-70 graduate jobs

LOCATIONS OF VACANCIES

Vacancies also available in Asia and elsewhere in the world.

STARTING SALARY FOR 2014

£29,000

Plus a performance-related bonus every year and a salary increase every 6 months.

UNIVERSITY VISITS IN 2013-14

ASTON, BATH, BIRMINGHAM, BRISTOL, CAMBRIDGE, DURHAM, IMPERIAL COLLEGE LONDON, LANCASTER, LEEDS, LIVERPOOL, LOUGHBOROUGH, MANCHESTER, NEWCASTLE, NOTTINGHAM, OXFORD, SURREY, UNIVERSITY COLLEGE LONDON, WARWICK

Please check with your university careers service for full details of local events.

MINIMUM ENTRY REQUIREMENTS

2.2 Degree

300 UCAS points

Relevant degree required for some roles.

APPLICATION DEADLINE

Year-round recruitment

Early application advised.

FURTHER INFORMATION

www.Top100GraduateEmployers.com

Register now for the latest news, events information and graduate recruitment details for Britain's leading employers.

WPP

www.wpp.com

hmiller@wpp.com

WPP is the world leader in communications services. Specialist skills include Advertising; Media Investment Management; Consumer Insight; PR & Public Affairs; Branding & Identity; Healthcare Communications; Direct, Digital, Promotion & Relationship Marketing and Specialist Communications.

WPP has over 150 companies setting industry standards and working with many of the world's leading brands, creating communications ideas that help to build business. Their clients include 350 of the Fortune Global 500, all of the Dow Jones 30, 63 of the NASDAQ 100 and 31 of the Fortune e-50. The Group also works with almost 360 clients across six or more countries. Collectively, WPP employs 165,000 people (including associates) in 3,000 offices in 110 countries.

WPP Marketing Fellowships develop high-calibre management talent with unique experience across a range of marketing disciplines. Over three years, Fellows work in three different WPP operating companies, each representing a different marketing communications discipline and geography. Each rotation is chosen on the basis of the individual's interests and the Group's needs.

Fellowships will be awarded to applicants who are intellectually curious and motivated by the prospect of delivering high-quality communications services to their clients. WPP wants people who are committed to marketing communications, take a rigorous and creative approach to problem-solving and will function well in a flexible, loosely structured work environment.

WPP is offering several three-year Fellowships, with competitive remuneration and excellent long term career prospects within WPP. Many former Fellows now occupy senior management positions in WPP companies across the world.

GRADUATE VACANCIES IN 2014

MARKETING

MEDIA

NUMBER OF VACANCIES

1-10 graduate jobs

LOCATIONS OF VACANCIES

Vacancies also available in Europe, Asia, the USA and elsewhere in the world.

STARTING SALARY FOR 2014

£Competitive

UNIVERSITY VISITS IN 2013-14

BRISTOL, CAMBRIDGE, KING'S COLLEGE LONDON, LONDON SCHOOL OF ECONOMICS, OXFORD, QUEEN MARY LONDON, ROYAL HOLLOWAY LONDON, UNIVERSITY COLLEGE LONDON

Please check with your university careers service for full details of local events.

MINIMUM ENTRY REQUIREMENTS

2.1 Degree

APPLICATION DEADLINE

7th November 2013

FURTHER INFORMATION

www.Top100GraduateEmployers.com

Register now for the latest news, events information and graduate recruitment details for Britain's leading employers.

01

Useful Information

EMPLOYER	GRADUATE RECRUITMENT WEBSITE
ACCENTURE	accenture.com/ukgraduates
AIRBUS	www.airbus.com/work
ALDI	www.aldirecruitment.co.uk
ALLEN & OVERY	www.aograduate.com
ARCADIA GROUP	www.arcadiagroup.co.uk/careers
ARMY	www.army.mod.uk/join/officer
ARUP	www.arup.com/careers
ASDA	www.ASDA.jobs/graduates
ATKINS	www.atkinsglobal.com/careers/graduates
BAKER & MCKENZIE	www.bakermckenzie.com/londongraduates
BALFOUR BEATTY	www.balfourbeatty.com/careers
BANK OF AMERICA MERRILL LYNCH	www.baml.com/campusEMEA
BARCLAYS	barclays.com/joinus
BBC	www.bbc.co.uk/careers
BLACKROCK	www.blackrockoncampus.com
BOOTS	www.boots.jobs/talentprogrammes
BOSTON CONSULTING GROUP	www.bcglondon.com
BP	bp.com/ukgraduates
BRITISH AIRWAYS	www.britishairwaysgraduates.co.uk
BT	www.btgraduates.com
CANCER RESEARCH UK	cruk.org/graduates
CENTRICA	www.centrica.com/graduates
CHANNEL 4	www.4Talent.com
CITI	www.oncampus.citi.com
CIVIL SERVICE FAST STREAM	www.faststream.civilservice.gov.uk
CLIFFORD CHANCE	www.cliffordchance.com/gradsuk
CO-OPERATIVE GROUP	www.co-operative.jobs
COCA-COLA ENTERPRISES	www.cokecce.com/careers
CREDIT SUISSE	credit-suisse.com/careers
DANONE	danone.co.uk/graduates
DELOITTE	www.deloitte.co.uk/graduates
DFID	www.dfid.gov.uk/graduate
DIAGEO	www.diageo.com/careers
DLA PIPER	www.dlapipergraduates.co.uk
EDF ENERGY	www.edfenergy.com/graduates
EUROPEAN COMMISSION (EU CAREERS)	www.eu-careers.eu
EY	ey.com/uk/careers
FRESHFIELDS BRUCKHAUS DERINGER	www.freshfields.com/uktrainees
GE	www.ge.com/uk/careers
GLAXOSMITHKLINE	www.gsk.com/careers/graduates.html
GOLDMAN SACHS	www.goldmansachs.com/careers
GOOGLE	www.google.com/students/emea
GRANT THORNTON	www.grant-thornton.co.uk/trainees
HERBERT SMITH FREEHILLS	herbertsmithfreehills.com/careers/london/graduates
HOGAN LOVELLS	www.hoganlovells.com/graduates
IBM	ibm.com/jobs/uk/graduate

EMPLOYER	GRADUATE RECRUITMENT WEBSITE
JAGUAR LAND ROVER	www.jaguarlandrovercareers.com
JOHN LEWIS PARTNERSHIP	www.jlpjobs.com/graduates
KPMG	www.kpmg.co.uk/times100
L'ORÉAL	www.lorealbusinessclass.co.uk
LIDL	www.lidlgraduatecareers.co.uk
LINKLATERS	www.linklaters.com/ukgrads
LLOYD'S	www.lloyds.com/TT100
LLOYDS BANKING GROUP	www.lloydsbankinggrouptalent.com
MARKS & SPENCER	www.marksandspencergrads.com
MARS	mars.co.uk/graduates
MCDONALD'S	www.mcdonalds.co.uk/people
MCKINSEY & COMPANY	www.mckinsey.com/careers
METROPOLITAN POLICE	www.metpolicecareers.co.uk
MI5	www.mi5.gov.uk/careers
MICROSOFT	www.microsoft.com/uk/graduates
MONDELĒZ INTERNATIONAL	www.mondelezukgraduates.co.uk
MORGAN STANLEY	www.morganstanley.com/careers
MORRISONS	www.morrisonsgraduates.com
NATIONAL GRID	www.nationalgridcareers.com/Development-Opportunities
NESTLÉ	www.nestleacademy.co.uk
NETWORK RAIL	www.networkrail.co.uk/graduates
NEWTON EUROPE	www.newtoneurope.com
NGDP	www.ngdp.org.uk
NHS	www.nhsgraduates.co.uk
OXFAM	www.oxfam.org.uk/get-involved/volunteer-with-us
PENGUIN	www.penguin.co.uk
PROCTER & GAMBLE	www.uki.experiencepg.com
PWC	www.pwc.com/uk/careers
ROLLS-ROYCE	www.rolls-royce.com/graduates
ROYAL AIR FORCE	www.raf.mod.uk/careers
ROYAL BANK OF SCOTLAND GROUP	rbsbankyoubuild.com
ROYAL NAVY	www.royalnavy.mod.uk/careers
SAINSBURY'S	sainsburys.jobs/graduates
SANTANDER	www.santanderukgraduates.com
SHELL	www.shell.com/graduate
SIEMENS	www.siemens.co.uk/careers
SKY	skygraduates.com
SLAUGHTER AND MAY	www.slaughterandmay.com
TEACH FIRST	www.teachfirst.org.uk/graduates
TESCO	www.tesco-graduates.com
THOMSON REUTERS	students.thomsonreuters.com
TRANSPORT FOR LONDON	www.tfl.gov.uk/graduates
UBS	www.ubs.com/graduates
UNILEVER	unilever.co.uk/careers-jobs/graduates
WPP	www.wpp.com